DIAGNOSIS AND REMEDIAL TEACHING IN ARITHMETIC

A

Other books by Fred J. Schonell

BACKWARDNESS IN THE BASIC SUBJECTS
THE PSYCHOLOGY AND TEACHING OF READING
ESSENTIALS IN TEACHING AND TESTING SPELLING
PRACTICE IN BASIC ARITHMETIC
RIGHT FROM THE START ARITHMETIC

With F. Eleanor Schonell

DIAGNOSTIC AND ATTAINMENT TESTING

By F. Eleanor Schonell

DIAGNOSTIC ENGLISH TESTS
EDUCATING SPASTIC CHILDREN

DIAGNOSIS AND REMEDIAL TEACHING IN ARITHMETIC

FRED J. SCHONELL, M.A., PH.D., D.LIT.

AND

F. ELEANOR SCHONELL, M.A., PH.D.

OLIVER AND BOYD

EDINBURGH : TWEEDDALE COURT

LONDON : 39A WELBECK STREET, W.1

Sole Agent for Canada
CLARKE, IRWIN & CO. LIMITED
TORONTO

First published 1957
Second impression 1958

Printed in Great Britain
by T. and A. CONSTABLE LTD , Hopetoun Street
Printers to the University of Edinburgh

PREFACE

RESULTS of educational research constantly emphasise the nature of individual differences in children's mental powers, in their learning rates and in the levels of their scholastic attainments, but it is doubtful if practical teaching has been sufficiently influenced by these findings. Although methods and materials have improved in most school subjects, yet there is need for some greater consideration of pupils' individual and particular requirements. Nowhere is this need so urgent as in arithmetic with its countless steps, its varied material and its numerous difficulties.

It is the primary purpose of this book to assist teachers in the prevention, diagnosis and remedying of pupils' difficulties in arithmetic. Experimental work over the past three decades has greatly increased our insight into pupils' mental processes involved during arithmetical learning and it is important that this information should be known by teachers so that they can prevent difficulties from arising. Hence the material of the first four chapters has a bearing on the prevention of failure in arithmetic. The various factors that enter arithmetical ability are listed, research findings on teaching methods in the basic processes are discussed and the common causes of backwardness in arithmetic are considered. For forewarned is very much forearmed where matters of arithmetical skill are concerned with children of different talents and temperaments, and, we should also add, of different home backgrounds.

But in spite of the progress in prevention that has come with vastly improved curricula and methods, arithmetic is still a stumbling-block for many pupils, and so the diagnostic and remedial aspects of the subject form a very important part of the primary school teacher's everyday work.

Once a pupil has experienced difficulty in arithmetic it is essential that he should receive some individual help, whether his handicap be a minor or a major one. Very often the right kind of help given in the early stages prevents confusion in the later stages and minimises the possibility of backwardness. Moreover, it should be remembered that progress in arithmetic is dependent as much upon emotional as upon intellectual factors and that individual consideration of pupils' difficulties is the best means of dispersing the psychological effects of failure. But if individual aid is to be fully effective it must be given systematically and produce positive results, and this is only possible where diagnosis has been both accurate and comprehensive.

It was to provide a means of systematic survey and accurate diagnosis of difficulties in arithmetic that the *Schonell Diagnostic Arithmetic Tests* were constructed. The Tests are so compiled that they cover all the basic number combinations in the four processes and all the important steps in each process, and hence use of them indicates exactly every unit or step in which pupils are failing. This knowledge, combined with information on causation of errors, enables teachers to distribute remedial practice to maximum advantage. The element of chance in arithmetic teaching is thereby minimised: the haphazard discovery of inaccurate knowledge is replaced by scientific analysis of achievements in all fundamentals. Such an analysis not only means that effective assistance can be given to pupils by use of carefully graded remedial work, but it also reveals information which can be utilised to frame positive teaching methods to prevent backwardness.

The progression that a remedial teaching programme might follow with pupils of varying levels of backwardness is given in the final section of the book. In this the kind of remedial material that should be used with each group of backward pupils is discussed in detail. There is now available to educational psychologists, guidance officers and teachers who use the *Diagnostic Arithmetic Tests*, a series of three books (*Practice in Basic Arithmetic*) which are closely related to the results of the diagnostic tests and provide suitably graded remedial material.

I wish to thank the Editorial Committee of *Educational Review* for permission to reprint some material in Chapters I and II that I had previously contributed to that journal.

August 1956

F. J. S.
F. E. S.

CONTENTS

CHAP. PAGE

I. FACTORS IN ARITHMETICAL ABILITY—INTELLIGENCE AND EXPERIENCE 1

Pattern of factors influencing arithmetical attainment. General intelligence. Research studies. Experience—general and school: (*a*) counting, (*b*) early experience of relationships between numbers, (*c*) common experience and its bearing on oral and problem arithmetic. Experience as a factor in problem arithmetic. Maturation

II. ARITHMETICAL ABILITY—OTHER FACTORS . . 21

Computational accuracy. Verbal ability. Visual imagery and spatial ability. Emotional attitudes. Temperament and emotional attitudes. Sex differences

III. RESEARCH RESULTS IN ARITHMETIC . . . 34

Changes in primary school syllabus. No decline in standards. Social value of arithmetic. Sections and individual work. Understanding followed by practice. Everyday applications of arithmetic. Methods in addition, subtraction and division

IV. BACKWARDNESS IN ARITHMETIC 56

A Environmental causes of backwardness in arithmetic
B Intellectual causes of backwardness in arithmetic
C Emotional causes of backwardness in arithmetic

V. DIAGNOSIS OF DIFFICULTIES IN ARITHMETIC . . 74

Nature and purpose of diagnostic tests

VI. THE SCHONELL DIAGNOSTIC ARITHMETIC TESTS : THEIR NATURE AND ADMINISTRATION 82

Nature of each test. General instructions for giving the tests. Marking and scoring the tests. Summary of the uses of the tests

VII. INTERPRETATION OF THE RESULTS 113

Averages of times taken for each test. Average scores for accuracy in given times. Schedules of common errors in the four processes. Summary of diagnostic information provided by the tests

CHAP. PAGE

VIII. Remedial Teaching in Arithmetic (First Stages) . 132

Five groups of pupils backward in arithmetic

GROUP 1 Extreme weakness in number combinations

Stage A Consolidation of number concepts

Stage B Practice in adding and subtracting by use of pictorial representations. Teaching relationship between addition and subtraction and between multiplication and division

Stage C Distributed drill with the basic number combinations

Stage D Distributed drill with higher decade extensions of the basic number facts. (*a*) Number combination cards for individual and group work, (*b*) Lotto, (*c*) Cobbler game, (*d*) Multiplication and division cards, (*e*) Jig-saw cards, (*f*) Number charts. Everyday applications of the basic number facts. Summary

IX. Remedial Teaching in Arithmetic (Further Stages) 166

GROUP 2 Pupils accurate but slow in basic number work. Improving multiplication and division

GROUP 3 Pupils with persistent individual errors

GROUP 4 Pupils weak in a particular aspect of a basic process. Need for grading of examples in remedial work. Remedial material in the four rules

GROUP 5 Less able pupils

APPENDIX I

Average Scores and Equivalent Arithmetic Ages for Diagnostic Arithmetic Tests 1—12 in Given Times 181

APPENDIX II

Answers to the Schonell Diagnostic Arithmetic Tests 1-12 190

INDEX 195

TABLES OF AGE GROUP AVERAGES FOR DIAGNOSTIC ARITHMETIC TESTS

	PAGE
Number of Sums Correct in Unlimited Time: Tests 6-12	115-7
Average Times taken to Complete Tests 1-11 . .	118-21
Average Scores and Equivalent Arithmetic Ages for Tests 1-12 in Given Times	181-9

SCHEDULES

A	Common Errors in Addition	123-4
B	Common Errors in Subtraction	125-6
C	Common Errors in Multiplication . . .	126-7
D	Common Errors in Division	128

DIAGNOSIS AND REMEDIAL TEACHING IN ARITHMETIC

CHAPTER I

FACTORS IN ARITHMETICAL ABILITY —INTELLIGENCE AND EXPERIENCE

WHAT accounts for the variations in the likes and dislikes for arithmetic among boys and girls at various ages and in various schools?

To answer this question we must look more closely at the factors or forces which underlie arithmetical attainments, for both intellectual factors and emotional attitudes as well as environmental conditions are linked with degree of success or failure in a subject. Moreover, it helps in the teaching of arithmetic to children of different ages, and in the avoidance of difficulties for them, if we know something of these factors. It helps if we can distinguish, amongst some of the factors at least, which are related to the intrinsic mental equipment of the pupil and which to the extrinsic or environmental aspects of the situation. This constitutes a challenge to us—a challenge to circumvent limitations of innate mental powers with some children, a challenge to improve teaching methods with all children. A logical and psychological analysis of the subject can be just as fruitful of suggestions for teaching as can the more specific and somewhat narrower examination of methods.

PATTERN OF FACTORS INFLUENCING ARITHMETICAL ATTAINMENT

A. *Achievement in mechanical arithmetic depends on:*

(*a*) general intelligence,
(*b*) experience: (i) general,
(ii) school,
(*c*) spatial ability (for mensuration and allied exercises),
(*d*) memory (of number combinations),
(*e*) computational knowledge of the four processes.

B. *Achievement in problem arithmetic depends on:*

(*a*) general intelligence } reasoning,
(*b*) experience: (i) general } reasoning,
(ii) school } reasoning,
(*c*) verbal ability,
(*d*) spatial ability,
(*e*) imagery,
(*f*) computational accuracy.

C. *Achievement in mental arithmetic depends on:*

(*a*) general intelligence,
(*b*) experience: (i) general,
(ii) school,
(*c*) auditory memory (if presented orally),
(*d*) visual imagery,
(*e*) memory of number combinations,
(*f*) computational accuracy.

In the following sections I shall first consider the various elements or factors which have a common influence on achievements in the three forms of arithmetic instruction as given in schools, and then later discuss those elements which relate more specifically to a particular form of arithmetical attainment.

General Intelligence

In the first place it does not require psychological experiment to establish the fact that ability to do arithmetic is fairly closely related to level of general intelligence or general mental ability. Teachers know from classroom experience that the brighter pupils more often succeed in arithmetic lessons, while the less able ones become confused, have difficulty in understanding the processes or in remembering their tables, and in many cases fail continuously in most aspects of their work. But teachers also know that there are variations, even among pupils of similar intelligence, from one pupil to another, from one class to another class, and in the same pupils in respect of their various achievements in mental arithmetic, mechanical arithmetic and problem arithmetic—which variations all suggest that there must be other factors involved in addition to general intelligence. And here psychological experiment can assist in sorting out the variables upon which levels of arithmetic achievement depend.

It is helpful to know just how much intelligence contributes to success in mechanical, problem and mental arithmetic and to know what are some of the other factors involved. By means of a statistical device known as correlation the psychologist can calculate the degree of relationship between measurable aspects of arithmetic. The correlation ratio he thus obtains is simply a statistical method of expressing the way in which two measures vary together.

Thus one way of indicating the extent to which arithmetical attainment is dependent upon general intelligence is to give tests of arithmetic and intelligence and then to calculate the degree to which scores in the arithmetic tests are related to scores in the intelligence tests. If the correspondence is perfect, that is, if the most intelligent pupil is always the best in arithmetic, while the next in intelligence is the next best in arithmetic and the pupil with the third highest score in intelligence obtains third highest arithmetic score and so on, till the one with the lowest intelligence score also gets the lowest arithmetic score, then this perfect positive correlation would be expressed as unity ($r=1{\cdot}00$). On the other hand, if the pupils with high intelligence scores sometimes got the lowest arithmetic scores and *vice versa*, the correlation coefficient would be a low one and would be of the nature of $r={\cdot}1$ or ${\cdot}2$. We know from classroom experience that neither of these coefficients adequately indicates the relationship between arithmetic and intelligence. While it is certainly not an absolute or perfect relationship—the influences of temperament and memory, and the conditions of teaching and learning have a bearing on achievements—yet we know that the relationship is a fairly high one.

Now educational research has a somewhat more refined method of unravelling the intellectual factors involved in an ability. A simple correlation can indicate the degree of relationship between general intelligence and arithmetic ability, but by itself it cannot reveal the proportional contribution of intelligence to the arithmetical process as a whole, nor can it indicate what other mental factors are involved in the ability. This can be done by calculating the relationships between arithmetical ability and other possible intellectual (cognitive) factors—intelligence, rote memory, number knowledge, reading comprehension, spatial ability and so on—and then discovering what are the relationships of each of these abilities to each other and to arithmetical ability. We can, by the method known as factor analysis, obtain a form of classification of the various factors involved in arithmetic ability, and by a simple step we can discover how much each of these factors contributes towards the total result.

However, in this more refined approach to the analysis of an ability through factor analysis, we need to be aware of two limitations. Firstly, the factors revealed by the statistical treatment represent only a form of classification and are not mental entities—actual abilities—themselves, although we may identify them with abilities and by other means prove that they are such. Secondly, this method cannot separate for us the part played by temperament, by emotional attitudes and by environmental conditions, such as good or bad teaching, which itself involves all kinds of conditions such as the actual methods used, the nature of the grading of examples and the kind of textbooks used. Nor does factor analysis indicate the relative contribution of different weekly time allocations to the subject with its closely related problem of the effect on arithmetical ability of absence from school at certain crucial times during primary education. But we can obtain fairly accurate information on the influence of all these forces on arithmetical ability by a combination of case study methods and by experiments involving the use of simple correlations and an analysis of variance.[1]

Or perhaps we may look at the results of our statistical analysis another way, and say that we need the cumulative evidence from the detailed study of many pupils as individuals to explain to us the exact nature of the factors revealed by a factor analysis.[2]

Research Studies

All studies of arithmetical ability and disability have indicated the importance of general intelligence (or a general or central factor) in ability to succeed in arithmetic. Thus Barakat, in a factor study of the mathematical ability of 160 boys and 160 girls in which he used a battery of tests of cognitive abilities and mathematical attainments, found that 'a basic or general ability roughly identifiable with innate intelligence appears to play by far the largest part in mathematical attainments of every kind'.[3] And Blackwell says 'this factor (*g*), in both

[1] A study which exemplifies the use of several statistical methods was that of M. K. Barakat entitled *Factors Underlying the Mathematical Abilities of Grammar School Pupils* (Ph.D. thesis, University of London, 1950), which employed (*a*) tests of cognitive abilities and mathematical attainments (intelligence, mechanical memory, arithmetic computation, etc.); (*b*) assessments of personal qualities (emotional stability, industry, etc.); and (*c*) environmental conditions. Factor analysis was used for the first set of measures, simple correlations for the second and analysis of variance for the third.

[2] Those interested in a more statistical and psychological discussion of the factors underlying mathematical ability as demonstrated in different investigations may consult *The Structure of Human Abilities*, by P. E. Vernon (Methuen, 1953). In this book Professor Vernon has ably summarised and discussed the relevance of factor analysis research for education.

[3] M. K. Barakat, *Factors Underlying the Mathematical Abilities of Grammar School Pupils* (Ph.D. thesis, University of London, 1950). Summary in *The British Journal of Educational Psychology*, November 1951, p. 239

sexes the most important component in mathematical ability, is described as the capacity for selective, quantitative thinking and deductive reasoning involving the ability to apply general principles to particular cases in number'.[1]

Similarly, Sutherland,[2] Vernon,[3] Coombs[4] and others all stress the very large part played by the general intellectual factor as compared with specific factors in arithmetic.

Supplementary evidence from a study of a different kind is brought forward by the Scottish Research Council in their examination of processes, methods and errors when they state that 'a pupil's success in an arithmetic topic, at whatever mental age he begins it, is to a considerable extent determined by I.Q.'[5]

Actually the relationship between arithmetic (including both problem and mechanical arithmetic) and intelligence yields an average correlation coefficient of ·7 (for different age groups). The form of the arithmetic determines the nature of the correlation coefficient and the following range of figures relates to different investigations from different groups of pupils of different ages and different levels of intelligence (in all cases pupils in each group used in each investigation were of the same age):

problem arithmetic=·7 to ·85;
mechanical arithmetic=·55 to ·72;
mental arithmetic=·65 to ·78.

Thus in the preparation of syllabuses in arithmetic and the application of teaching methods there is the need to take into fuller consideration the fact that general intelligence is an *important* factor in determining success in arithmetic, whether

[1] A. M. Blackwell, Factors Involved in Mathematical Ability, *Br. J. Educ. Psych.*, November 1940, p. 221

[2] J. Sutherland, An Investigation into some Aspects of Problem Solving in Arithmetic, *Br. J. Educ. Psych.*, November 1941 and February 1942

[3] P. E. Vernon, Educational Abilities of Training College Students, *Br. J. Educ. Psych.*, November 1939

[4] C. H. Coombs, A Factorial Study of Number Ability, *Psychometrica*, Vol. 6, pp. 161-189

[5] *Studies in Arithmetic*, Vol. 2, p. 215. Scottish Council for Research in Education. Publication No. XVIII (University of London Press, 1944)

problem, mechanical or mental. Practice shows that insufficient attention has been paid to this in the demands still made of many children in some problem arithmetic and in the syllabuses still used for classes of dull pupils. Undoubtedly both such conditions have improved of recent years—we no longer set the bulk of our pupils of 9 or 10 advanced problems demanding a mental age of 11 or 12 years, and examination papers for the selection of pupils for secondary schools no longer contain the unfamiliar problems that caused difficulty even to the teachers themselves. There is, however, the further need, as I shall indicate later, to eliminate the difficult, unreal problems from the arithmetic syllabus of the junior school and the secondary modern school and to reduce in extent of topics, and in the size of the numbers used, the syllabus for dull and backward (educationally subnormal) pupils. Apart from functional considerations of the unreal or overloaded syllabuses, less able pupils are predestined to failure when the arithmetic topics they attempt demand a higher mental age for starting, or a better I.Q. for understanding and applying the relationships they involve.

It will be noted that general intelligence contributes a greater share towards ability in problem arithmetic than in mechanical arithmetic and thus it is more difficult to produce improvement in solving problems than in doing mechanical sums. There is continuous evidence of these differences in that some bright pupils are often better at problem exercises than at mechanical arithmetic, and this is particularly so if the computational element in the problems is slight. In solving an arithmetical problem it is sorting out the data, making the inferences and selecting the appropriate method that require intelligence.

Furthermore, less able pupils may reach, through effective teaching, a normal standard in mechanical arithmetic, but may only be able to reach a standard 25 or even 30 per cent. lower on the same or simpler processes framed in problem form. It is therefore important to discover what are the other elements entering into the three forms of arithmetic commonly given in schools and thereby, in so far as degree of innate intelligence cannot be altered, to concentrate on the improvable factors entering into arithmetic achievement.

Experience—General and School

Perhaps the most important experience of a general kind is that relating to the formation of number concepts and number vocabulary and to the early basis of simple spatial knowledge. The manner in which children form these concepts and gather this verbal and spatial knowledge is dependent partly on their intellectual power, but also, to a considerable degree, upon the nature and extent of their experience with a variety of concrete materials in all sorts of situations. The success achieved at this stage conditions the success and understanding that children will display in much of their subsequent calculation. Much failure and backwardness in arithmetic is due to pushing pupils along too fast, *i.e.* dealing with figures without having formed a number sense for them, and in this the school is often to blame, not the child. The father who said his children could do arithmetic until they went to school was quite right. It is imperative that pupils should be given, in the initial stages of number, every possible opportunity of forming sensible and lasting concepts by discovering the meaning of number for themselves through a variety of experiences with concrete materials of different kinds. Naturally some homes provide the material and situations for this *incidental* learning, and this is one of the functions that a nursery school or class can so well assume. Figures from the interim report of the Scottish Council for Research in Education reveal a very wide range in the knowledge with which pupils enter school. 'Whereas almost all pupils (*i.e.* entrants at 5+) can perform rote counting by units (96 per cent. count up to 5, 86 per cent. up to 10 and 61 per cent. up to 15, but only 30 per cent. up to 20), only 20 per cent. can accomplish rote counting by tens.

Over 90 per cent. of school entrants can give 2 objects, over 50 per cent. can give 5 objects and over 20 per cent. can give 10 objects when they are required to do so by the teacher, and when the pupils are asked to name the number of objects presented, the results are practically identical, although it has generally been assumed that to give the number names is the more difficult 'process'.[1]

The finding that only 54 per cent. can recognise 5 objects and 36 per cent. 6 objects is of particular significance to teachers in this early work. It emphasises the slow development in understanding what numbers mean,[2] and it indicates strongly that our first stage in number work might deal with numbers up to 5.

Tests of counting, counting with enumeration, matching, recognition or number selection, and recall of groups of numbers showed that there are many children at 5+ and 6+ who are not ready to do any formal work, and who need much more experience of concrete situations. It would be advantageous for teachers to apply the tests (given in the report) to pupils after they have entered school. They would thus get some idea of the range in background of their pupils, and more particularly of those who required six or more months' incidental learning before commencing number in a more formal sense.

(a) *Counting*

Many pupils when they first enter school may be able to count up to 12 or 15 or even 20, but the serial order is recited in much the same way as a nursery rhyme. The counting is not meaningful, for when objects are shown, the pupils fail to give many numbers their correct cardinal values. Early ability in arithmetic which rests upon counting must be more than a mere repetition of names. The repetitive aspect is only a psychological response to rhythmical movement; to be meaningful number must pass far beyond that level, although of course counting is the basis of all early number work and a child's counting exceeds his understanding of number relationships. A point of psychological interest is that relating to the movement that accompanies counting. Many pupils count aloud more quickly than they can count silently, a fact which is in marked contrast to reading, in which silent reading is much

[1] *The Early Development of Number Concepts*, S.C.R.E. Publication XX (University of London Press, 1942), p. 27

[2] More than two-thirds of the pupils fail completely on the ordinal numbers and only 10 per cent. know 'fourth' and 5 per cent. 'fifth'.

quicker than oral. It would seem that in counting some kind of involuntary movement is necessary to put the mental mechanism into operation. It is for this reason that children (and some adults) use their fingers, make marks, wag their heads, tap or move their lips when they are counting. It is obviously unsound psychologically to prevent young pupils from using this material aid when they are calculating. Naturally, useless habits must be prevented from developing, but until the fundamental combinations in the four rules have reached a fair level of automatic accuracy by frequent systematically distributed practice, it is necessary to let many junior pupils make full use of crutches, particularly the use of counters.

Counting should proceed from the first psychological stage of the names of the numbers to an application of the names to external objects. Here the children's immediate surroundings, the activities they take part in, the articles they use and the objects around them can all be made the basis of number development. 'How many spoons do we want?' 'How many pencils are wanted?' 'How many books for this row?' 'How many bottles of milk left over?' etc. No attempt should be made at this stage to deal with these number situations in a 'combination way', as in '2 pencils are needed in this row and 3 pencils in that row. How many pencils is that altogether?'—this kind of number experience is best left until the children have a complete understanding of unit and group values. Variety, as in other concept formation, is essential so that activities such as jumping, hopping, clapping, skipping so many times, together with the carrying out of instructions involving numbers, aid materially in consolidating the meanings of numbers. Useful as it is to all children, this activity work is particularly valuable to dull children, who seem to understand number elements best through situations in which they take part. I have seen dull pupils suddenly acquire an idea of a number such as five when they have been forced to procure another chair for a group of five persons, or when they have had to see that each of five pupils has a book. Although the visual sense plays an important part in the acquisition of number concepts, yet the auditory (through rhythmic work), the tactile and the kinaesthetic senses are none the less useful channels of number knowledge.

The idea to be developed on the basis of counting is that of grouping, so that the pupil will know, through his activity work in varying situations with different materials, that 4, 5 or 6, as the case may be, means a collection of 4, 5 or 6 objects of any kind. At this stage, understanding the relationships between the numbers—that 2 and 2, and 3 and 1 both make a group of 4—should not be the objective, though if such knowledge is acquired *incidentally* so much the better.

Furthermore, there should not be any hurry to introduce pupils to the symbols that represent the numbers, for if the concrete experience is varied, vivid and comprehensive, then the assimilation of abstractions, however elementary, will be much easier.

(*b*) *Early Experience of Relationships between Numbers*

When a satisfactory stage has been reached in counting and in the development of the concept of number as a group, it is essential that this should be extended to include some idea of the elementary relationships between numbers up to 5. Through actual experiences the pupils should be led to understand that groups of numbers can be combined to form a larger group and that when an object or several objects are taken from a group then a smaller group is formed. This is the meaningful basis for addition and subtraction but it is achieved through concrete activities without any reference to signs. Naturally unit relationships combined with group ideas form the first steps, thus:

1 counter and 1 more make a group of 2.
2 counters and 1 more make a group of 3.
3 counters and 1 more make a group of 4.
4 counters and 1 more make a group of 5.

Then steps such as :

1 stick and 2 more make a group of 3.
2 sticks and 2 more make a group of 4.
3 sticks and 2 more make a group of 5.

Similarly, steps in the reverse way build up a basis for subtraction and also emphasise the relationship between addition and subtraction. Because this stage in the development of number ability represents for young children a more difficult mental operation than they have previously encountered it cannot be hurried. There are some pupils who grasp the relationships comparatively quickly while others need repetition after repetition of the concrete experiences before the meaning of the relationship really unfolds itself and before their memories will retain it for any length of time. In some cases the slowness is due to intellectual deficiency while in others it is due to insufficient meaningful experience with counting and with groups.

Until this level of elementary number relationships has been reached in varied concrete situations it is idle to introduce pupils to even the simplest formal work in addition or subtraction involving abstract symbols and still more abstract and less understood signs.

Although the foregoing step is of paramount importance, it is surprising how often it is omitted from children's number work. The tendency is, after counting and grouping, to hurry pupils on to the names of the symbols, to matching symbols and quantities and then to the formal step of introducing them to the addition sign followed by simple addition and subtraction combinations with the aid of concrete materials. Yet the pupil is often held up in his later work by insufficient knowledge of the idea of combining numbers and of splitting groups.

Most of the difficulty in arithmetic arises because we hurry pupils too much in the early stages.[1] The wild statements that some of them make about relative sizes and about fundamentals in the four processes show that their conception of number is

[1] The New Zealand Education Department has made a strong attempt to induce the teachers in its schools not to do any formal work with pupils before a mental age of 6+ and to assist in this they have issued an admirable booklet, *Number Work in the Infant Room—Some Suggestions for Teachers*, School Publications Branch, New Zealand Education Department.

Examples of equally well-planned information in the early stages of teaching arithmetic are to be found in the excellent publication of the New South Wales Department of Education, *Curriculum for Primary Schools* (1952), pp. 199-245, and in *The Method of Teaching Arithmetic* (Education Department, Victoria, 1944), pp. 15-71.

faulty. When a pupil gives 14 as an answer to 16—12 it shows that his knowledge of the meaning of number is insufficient. And so with all children who experience difficulty in arithmetic, whatever their age, it will be found that their conceptions of the meaning of number need further development. Irrespective of their class or age such pupils should be taken back to the beginning and once more given a grounding in number concepts. Failure in arithmetic is the result of half-understood knowledge, and once failure begins it is difficult to disperse its effects.

(c) *Common Experience and its Bearing on Oral and Problem Arithmetic*

The nature and extent of the common or everyday experience of the pupils, the way this is extended and the use that is made of it, have an important bearing on instruction in oral and problem arithmetic. For these forms of arithmetic demand above all else reasoning ability, and although this depends to a considerable extent upon general intelligence, yet there are three experiential elements which are acquired and hence susceptible of improvement. These are (i) knowledge of familiar situations which involve or may involve numbers; (ii) knowledge of different types of problems; (iii) reading attainment.

All good education seeks to widen a pupil's general experience and some schools and some methods do this more successfully than others. Activity work, practical activities and projects all tend to widen general experience more effectively than formal teaching methods, and it is for this reason that many schools, adopting a vigorous activity programme, surprise the 'formalists' by achieving results in the basic subjects quite as good as, and sometimes superior to, the formal schools—this is provided that 'activity' schools also make some systematically planned provision for a certain amount of instruction in the mechanics of spelling, reading and arithmetic. The over-ardent 'activity school' sometimes falls down on this, and the pupils as a result become confused and backward in the basic skills.

Experience gained from an activity programme gives pupils

the background of understanding so valuable for their verbal and arithmetical studies. A useful report[1] (recently reprinted) states: 'We strongly urge that activity in measuring, weighing, fitting and shopping should continue to be an essential part of the arithmetic course throughout the Primary school and that children should be led to regard the recording of such experiences as of equal importance with the working of the "sums".'

An important element in all reasoning is experience. The young child is often held up in his ability to reason, not by his level of general intelligence but by his lack of experience, and, within the limits of his experience, he often astounds us by the degree of reasoning ability he displays.

The point of practical teaching significance is that through activities, through visits, through actual handling of objects and materials, we should endeavour to supplement and extend the experience of our pupils, and then all oral and problem arithmetic should be framed, as far as possible, in terms of this experience. The more we succeed in doing this, the more will our pupils succeed in problem arithmetic, for problems, oral or written, in terms of familiar or common experiences give pupils a chance to understand what the sum demands, and enable them to make inferences in terms of familiar concepts. Moreover, visual imagery is readily and quickly evoked to assist the reasoning.

Experience as a Factor in Problem Arithmetic

An analysis of certain series of textbooks in arithmetic revealed that the problems included in the books demanded knowledge of over 2200 different situations or experiences, many of which were unfamiliar to the pupils and hence prevented them from using their intelligence effectively.

In Sutherland's experiment[2] with 134 children aged 11+,

[1] *Arithmetic in Primary Schools, A Report on the Teaching of Arithmetic and Spatial Knowledge in Primary Schools*, Association of Teachers in Colleges and Departments of Education, 2nd ed. revised (Longmans Green, 1947)

[2] J. Sutherland, An Investigation into Some Aspects of Problem Solving in Arithmetic, *Br. J. Educ. Psych.*, November 1941 and February 1942

with a mean I.Q. of 94, two groups of pupils equal in age and intelligence did tests in arithmetic problems, some of which dealt with familiar situations and some with unfamiliar, but comparable in all other respects. The results showed most conclusively that the familiar situation problems produced 36 per cent. improvement in scores, and in the case of the least able quarter of the pupils no less than 83 per cent. improvement in scores. The writer concludes: 'Since the object of education is to equip the child for life, and since only a very small minority will ever find themselves in unfamiliar situations, it is reasonable to suppose that we should concentrate on the simple little problems dealing with the things in our immediate neighbourhood. In this way it will be possible to let the children see some object in arithmetic, and children of all ages will come to realise that problem work is the rational form of arithmetic instead of something tacked on to make the subject more difficult than it really is.'

While preparing the revision of this little book I received from one of my graduate students[1] a copy of a test which he has specially compiled for his work in the Territory of Papua and New Guinea. In order to obtain maximum understanding of the arithmetical concepts involved he has, as the following samples show, framed his test questions to fit into the background experiences of his pupils:

1. There are three women and two men over there. How many people are there altogether?

2. The village people had ten pigs. They killed one for the feast. How many pigs did they kill?

3. How many pigs were left?

4. I have four yams in the basket, two yams on the ground, and one yam in my hand. How many yams altogether?

5. Twelve taro plants were growing in the garden. The pigs dug up four. How many were left?

[1] Kindly sent to me by G. T. Roscoe, Assistant Director of Education in Papua and New Guinea

6. Six people were sitting in the house, and four more came in. How many people altogether?

7. The first girl had three coconuts, the second girl had two coconuts, and the third girl had four coconuts. How many coconuts altogether?

8. We have twelve mangoes. Three are too green to eat, and four are rotten. The rest are just right for eating. How many are just right for eating?

Mr Roscoe informs me that while many native children in New Guinea have difficulty in tackling sums in the form in which they are framed for children in other countries, they can all attempt sums of this kind with varying degrees of success.

Of course, modern primary arithmetic is increasingly dealing with the familiar. Thus the pupil has a fair chance of solving such problems as these:

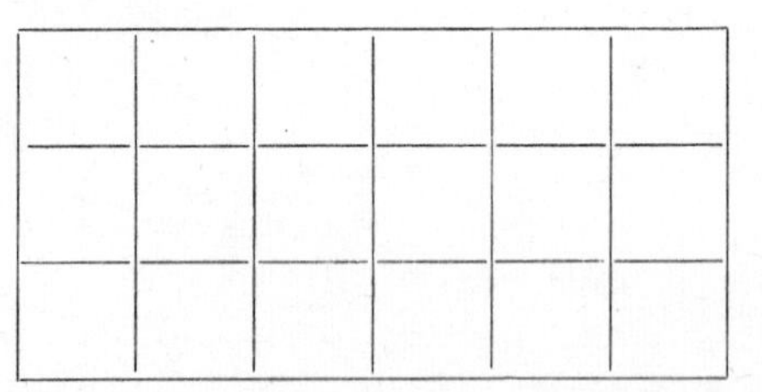

1. Here is a tray of milk bottles. How many bottles does it hold? Three bottles make up a pint. How many pints are there in a tray?

2. Here is a price list [price list given]. Two boys were sent to the shop to get these things. How much did each spend?

James	*John*
7 lbs. of potatoes	2 lbs. of parsnips
a cabbage of 3 lbs.	10 lbs. of potatoes
2 lbs. of apples	2 bunches of turnips
2 lbs. of carrots	2 lbs. of pears

3. Each day I get 2 pints of milk at 7½d. per pint. How much should I pay the milkman each week?

For brighter pupils of 10+, or for seniors of 11+ or 12+, a post office project permits the introduction of information valuable in everyday life, and provides a basis for much functional arithmetic set against a background of experience. Thus may be explained to pupils the means by which money can be sent by letter from one place to another. Postal orders can be purchased, filled in and cashed at a post office. The use and rates of poundage can be explained and a list of the rates drawn up for use in the classroom. Then exercises may be given on buying postal orders for certain amounts.

Real-life situations may be reflected in problems which include the cost of mailing certain amounts together with the cost of the stamp for the letter. Similar information can be gathered and used in connection with the postage of letters, newspapers and parcels, and the sending of telegrams. Some problem arithmetic can be framed in terms of situations which occur in everyday life, or are known to pupils through project or activity work. Plenty of examples of situations which give natural practice in the use of money and common weights and measures present themselves as a basis for the arithmetic of senior boys and girls who leave school at 15; for example, estimating the comparative costs of articles bought outright and by hire purchase, series of lessons based on housekeeping costs, on furnishing a room, on making a garage, or on the everyday problem of obtaining information from a bus or train time-table. One group of boys, aged 12-13 years, learned almost as much geography of the British Commonwealth during their arithmetic project based on international air time-tables as they did in a previous year's formal study of the British Commonwealth. All such arithmetic not only has functional value of an arithmetical kind but often provides useful general information.

There is still too much formal, unreal problem arithmetic in some textbooks, particularly those for secondary modern schools and junior forms of grammar schools. Sums about the times taken to do certain unreal tasks, about men building walls and mowing meadows, or trains, cars and cyclists engaged in races, exercises on changing francs to dollars and then to rupees, quite artificial problems on tiling, paving, papering, etc.—these and many other such exercises have little relation to life, serve little purpose and have little appeal even to bright pupils, and in so far as the examples represent unfamiliar situations the pupils are thus handicapped in solving them.

An important principle in respect to problem arithmetic is that every step or stage in mechanical arithmetic should be followed by its equivalent in problem (or better called 'puzzle') form. This procedure means that pupils become accustomed to the form and pattern of problems in relation to the successive steps they learn in mechanical arithmetic—problems are not something taught once a week and reserved for tests or for mental arithmetic. But the numbers used in the problems should be small, in order to reduce computation to a minimum, and all sorts of everyday situations of school, home and life should be employed. Records of classroom practice show that if this procedure of teaching problems is adopted, then, to some extent, we circumvent or lessen the emphasis placed on intelligence as a requisite for solving problem sums.

Thus in the early stages of arithmetic teaching we should aim to give a large number of very simple one-step problems of this kind:[1]

1. 3 boys in one row did not have milk, and 5 boys in the next. How many was this?
2. Tom had 9 marks and lost 2. So he had — left.
3. There are 4 rows in a class. In each row are 9 children. How many children are there in a class?
4. A card holds 6 buttons. How many cards must I buy to get 30 buttons?

These in turn should be followed, at their correct places in the arithmetic scheme, by a large number of simple two-step problems, each coming after similar mechanical arithmetic, so that the experience of the form is given its maximum emphasis. Examples of these might be:

[1] This naturally involves the level of reading attainments of the pupils, the vocabulary used in the simple problems and the amount of training in reading comprehension given to the pupils. These points will be dealt with later.

1. In a cricket match our class scored 31 runs and the other side 6 less. How many runs were scored altogether? (Addition and subtraction.)

2. Father bought 2 tram tickets at 4d. each and 2 at 3d. each. How much altogether? (Multiplication and addition.)

3. I buy 4 stamps at $2\frac{1}{2}$d. each. How much left from 1s.? (Multiplication and subtraction.)

In this way school experience may be allied to everyday experience to step up the element of familiarity for the pupils. The element of newness and the need for inference (a vital step in the process of reasoning) are thus reduced by the ease with which the pupil recognises both the form of the problem and the familiarity of its setting.

If we could always follow in our teaching the sequence (*a*) *experience*, (*b*) *use*, (*c*) *test for understanding*, we should prevent much failure in arithmetic, for to a considerable degree inability to progress is due to the confusion which follows insecure knowledge. We can often lead pupils to step (*b*) without going through step (*a*), but this deficiency is usually shown up in step (*c*). It is easy to tell a child that there are 2 pints in a quart, 4 quarts in a gallon and 8 pints in a gallon, and we may get him to do simple sums involving pints, quarts and gallons, but unless there is adequate experience of these facts in real situations he may later either forget the figures 2, 4 and 8, or he may not know whether he should multiply or divide by them. Similarly it is not difficult to get pupils working correctly straightforward sums depending on the knowledge, told or demonstrated only, that the area of a rectangle is found by multiplying length by breadth, or that its perimeter 'equals twice length plus breadth, $P=2(L+B)$'. Pupils who receive this knowledge in an artificial way soon reveal confusion in the nature of the measures they use.

There is a very great need in the primary school for building up an understanding by means of practical and activity work using and extending the pupils' experience. This may mean that we have to do less and do it more thoroughly, but at least we shall give pupils a training in mathematical thinking instead of finding that some of them either react in a semi-automatic way or become so confused that they cannot succeed with mathematics of any kind.

Maturation

A note should be added in regard to maturation of pupils as an element in arithmetical ability. Obviously increased maturation will, with most pupils, improve their chances of success in arithmetic for they have increased their experience and their mental age, and in this maturation intelligence is a more important factor than special experience. Metcalfe Smith[1] compared pupils from pairs of Infant schools in which one of each pair 'gave regular number lessons from the age of 5 and no period of play or creative activity, while in the corresponding school no formal lessons were given before the children were 6, and considerable emphasis was put on a daily period of play and creative activity'. Special number knowledge tests were given at 6-, 7-, and 9-year-old levels.

Analysis of the results from the research showed that, at the age of 6, differences between the schools were negligible and certain stages in the development of number concepts seemed common to all children. 'Differences were more marked as the children grew older, but even so the common characteristics suggest a limitation due to maturation in the idea it is possible for the children to assimilate from any teaching at each stage.'[2]

Smith's tests given at the 9-year-old level showed significant differences in three out of four aspects of number knowledge in favour of the informal schools, a result in keeping with those of Miss D. E. M. Gardner's *Testing Results in the Infant School* (Methuen). Smith's research also emphasised what the Scottish Council's researches also showed, namely the over-riding importance of intelligence and increases in intellectual maturity in children's development in understanding arithmetical concepts and processes.

[1] M. Metcalfe Smith, *An Investigation into the Development of Number Concepts in Young Children* (M.A. thesis, University of Leeds)

[2] From a summary kindly provided by Miss Metcalfe Smith.

CHAPTER II

ARITHMETICAL ABILITY—OTHER FACTORS

Computational Accuracy

Although general intelligence and experience are both vital contributors to progress in arithmetic, there is the need to realise that achievement at later levels is dependent upon a fairly speedy working efficiency in the basic number combinations. A pupil may have the requisite intelligence and experience, and may consistently display a combination of these in his arithmetic through his adequate knowledge of processes and his effective reasoning ability, but may consistently fail to get the right answers. Thus in mechanical sums he may select the right process and carry out all the correct steps, and still get most of his work wrong; or in problem arithmetic he may develop all the correct reasoning and show that he understands the problem, only to fail continuously in his calculations. As I shall show later, this recurring inaccuracy may be due to emotional conditions or to temperamental traits of the pupil, but much more frequently it is due to insufficient properly planned practice with the basic number facts in the four rules.[1]

Hence there is in arithmetical attainment a further element, namely, computational accuracy, which, though deriving partly from the degree to which pupils understand the basic number combinations, also derives from the amount of scientifically distributed practice they have been given in the classroom.

But there are certain essentials to be observed in providing practice in the basic number facts—addition and subtraction of numbers up to 18, *i.e.* 1+1 and 1−1 up to 9+9 and 18−9,

[1] American research has shown that even in more advanced work—fractions, decimals and percentages—a considerable proportion of the errors is due to computational inaccuracy.

and the multiplication and division tables up to and including 12 times. In the first place *practice without understanding pays poor dividends, but also understanding without plenty of practice yields similarly reduced results.* The former approach is that of the formalist, the blind believer in drill, the latter that of the theorist (sometimes ill-informed on arithmetic in primary schools) who believes that pupils will 'pick up' their number combinations if they have experienced them through concrete situations and applications in sums. He takes this stand partly as a reaction against much of the older hit-or-miss drill, which was often neither planned nor distributed for individual requirements, and partly because he thinks that drill (practice) is distasteful to the child. In the first part of his reaction he is right, in the second he is wrong. There is nothing that pupils of 7 to 11 like better than checking their number facts, or doing them as lots of 'little sums', particularly if they are getting many of them right. This procedure fits in with the psychology of the period—the child's desire for repetitive action through which he can master fundamental material and thus gain a sense of power.

Meddleton recently completed an excellent piece of work[1] in which he demonstrated that the systematic use of scientifically compiled sheets of number combinations gives results in arithmetic attainments superior to the usual hit-or-miss, unplanned drills of the classroom. He worked with two experimental and two control groups of pupils in London schools from areas of contrasting social background. Initial tests of intelligence and arithmetic attainment were given to the experimental group (135 pupils) and the control group (127 pupils). Then over a period of five months the experimental group worked systematically each day over forty sheets of number combinations in addition, subtraction, multiplication and division, while in the control group teachers were simply asked to give their classes practice in the number combinations for ten minutes each day.

[1] Ivor G. Meddleton, *An Experimental Investigation into the Systematic Teaching of Number Combinations in Arithmetic* (unpublished Ph.D. thesis, University of London, 1954)

Careful statistical checks and treatment of the results were made throughout and at the end of the investigation by means of an analysis of co-variance in which the factors of initial arithmetical ability and intelligence were taken into account. After allowing for any variations between the groups in terms of intelligence or initial arithmetical attainments, the experimental group was found to have made statistically significant gains over the control group in mechanical arithmetic (1 per cent. level), in problem arithmetic (·1 per cent. level), and also in addition, subtraction, multiplication and division (all at ·1 per cent. level), a gain which was maintained after a vacation.

But other interesting results came from the study. Meddleton was able to show that by use of systematically compiled material most gain was made in the division process. This is evidence of a constructive kind on how teachers can improve the division attainments of many children. He also showed that an appreciable amount of computational accuracy transferred to problem arithmetic.

An analysis of the material used by the experimental and control class revealed that the control schools gave more practice in addition and multiplication combinations, and tended to neglect subtraction and division. But the experimental class, because it used properly prepared material, was given adequate practice in the combinations in all four processes in the same time allowed each day. For example, during the first thirty-eight days of the investigation, the control pupils had practice with an average of twenty-seven number combinations a day, while the experimental pupils gained practice with an average of forty-eight per day.

A comparison of the total number of combinations used by each of the groups is as follows:

Group	Addition	Subtraction	Multiplication	Division	Total
Exp.	610	375	313	504	1802
Cont.	415	157	271	182	1025

It was interesting to note that the superior results in arithmetical attainments of pupils in the experimental classes were achieved quite effectively as part of the ordinary school teaching programme. This study provides the most carefully checked statistical evidence to date of the marked advantage to teachers of following a systematic programme with properly prepared material in order to develop accuracy and speed in the number combinations.

Both experience and practice should be combined to give the best results from work with number combinations or tables. For this reason children in the lower classes of the junior school should be allowed, in the first place, to build up multiplication and division tables from counters, while less able groups should be permitted to employ counters for doing their number drill (from prepared sheets or books) where they find it necessary.

Research results show that children who are in the first place permitted to build up their tables from the concrete by using counters, and so 'discover' them, later following this with memorisation of the tables, are in general quicker and more accurate than those who learn them blindly as tables provided by the teacher.

The nature of modern drill material, together with information on its construction and its use, is discussed fully in Chapters VIII and IX.

Verbal Ability

Of the remaining factors influencing arithmetic ability (see Table on page 2) three others call for some consideration. These are verbal ability, power of visual imagery and spatial ability, and emotional attitudes.

A number of research studies have in various ways demonstrated the importance of a verbal factor in arithmetic when the material is couched in words, as in problem arithmetic and mental arithmetic. But results from studies of verbal ability in arithmetic have been somewhat misleading and conflicting in regard to the actual part played by the verbal factor in mental and problem arithmetic. A reading of the research literature seems to suggest that this has been so because investigators have not defined exactly what they meant by verbal ability, and have not subdivided, so to speak, the elements of verbal ability that enter into non-mechanical forms of arithmetic. I think we can correctly define two aspects of verbal ability that enter into arithmetic:

(i) nature and extent of vocabulary, *i.e.* knowledge of words, particularly those used frequently in arithmetic; and

(ii) power to reason using the ideas expressed in sentences as the material for reasoning.

This verbal reasoning power is, in a sense, only intellectual power revealing itself in a verbal situation, but facilitated in that situation if the pupil has a good understanding of words. That is, the two aspects of verbal ability (i) and (ii) frequently act together, but a pupil may have ability in (i) without necessarily having ability in (ii). There are children who have a fairly wide vocabulary but who are weak in verbal reasoning.

Reading comprehension is a form of verbal reasoning and for that reason improvement in reading comprehension usually brings some improvement in problem solving.[1] However, problems involve both words and numbers and may involve quite complex relationships. While it would not seem possible to increase a pupil's actual power to understand relationships, yet it would seem possible to help pupils to develop a technique in noting relevant statements, neglecting irrelevant ones and reading correctly the numbers involved. The degree of improvement that such training produces in pupils is dependent on their levels of intelligence and on the extent to which we can develop their arithmetic vocabularies.

And in this respect we must remember that vocabulary cannot be expanded just by telling children the meanings of words or giving them lists of words to learn. Vocabulary grows through usage and the more chances a child has of using the vocabulary of arithmetic in real situations, the more likely is he really to understand the words, assimilate them and use them. Pupils understand units of length, of area, of weight,

[1] See *The Relationship of Reading Skills to the Ability to Solve Problems*, *J. Educ. Res.*, No. 38, pp. 86-98.

with their associated terms of longer, shorter, wider, heavier etc., if they have a chance actually to use these terms in concrete situations. Training of that kind will enable them to understand sums when set in problem form.

Training in reading problems has been found to reduce premature generalisation, to decrease errors due to incorrect transcription and to prevent loss of confidence when dealing with rather wordy problems.

Visual Imagery and Spatial Ability

There is evidence that imagery, that capacity to hold in front of the mind's eye the imaginary figures used in making a mental calculation, or the imaginary diagram needed for a train of reasoning, plays some part in arithmetical ability. So strong is visual imagery in some children that the images they evoke are almost as strong as the actual perception—they can almost 'see' the figures involved in oral or mental calculations.

Many children reveal the use to which they put imagery in recalling tables and in solving certain kinds of problems, particularly where the information given is best assembled by the aid of an imaginary diagram and inferences made from it. How many of the readers, for example, find themselves using visual imagery in solving this problem?

A large cube, painted red on every side, is cut into 27 smaller cubes.

How many cubes have red on three sides?
How many cubes have red on two sides only?
How many cubes have red on one side only?
How many cubes have no red at all?

There is classroom evidence, not checked, so far as I know, by controlled experiment, to show that when pupils are given practice in using visual imagery by closing their eyes and shutting out overt stimuli, some of them make a noticeable improvement in what they can recall and in their scores in mental arithmetic.

Connected with visual imagery is spatial ability. Success in some parts of the arithmetic curriculum, particularly mensuration and problems related to it, would appear to depend in a small measure on the pupils' spatial ability. And some investigations using factor analysis have given statistical evidence of this relationship between the spatial factor and arithmetical ability.

Practical work involving lines, angles, shapes and division of shapes, besides laying the foundations for later work in geometry, can be an essential element of successful work in simple mensuration. For example, it is valueless and artificial to teach areas unless pupils have had sufficient experience of handling pieces of wood or cardboard, of measuring them and finding out how many 'squares big' they are. Pieces of cardboard of different sizes (3 inches by 2, 4 inches by 2, 4 inches by 3, 6 inches by 3, etc.) can be provided for the pupils to measure and rule up in this way:

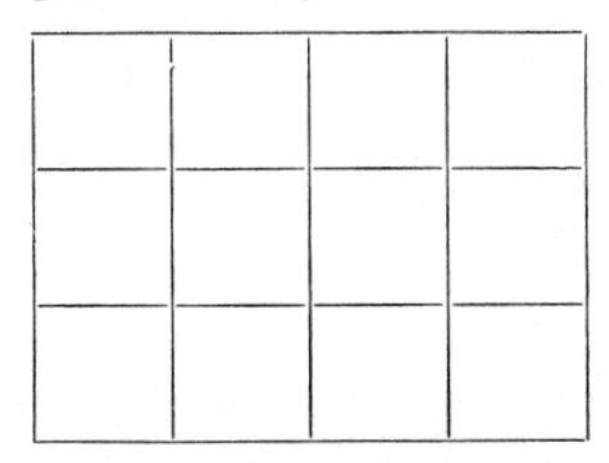

From such practical work they can determine the number of 'squares big' that each piece of cardboard is, and then deduce the formula for area.

Undoubtedly the development of spatial ability in primary school pupils is connected to some extent with the nature and extent of training they obtain in dealing with shapes, sizes, position and familiar units of weights and measures. An arithmetic syllabus which introduces practical work of all kinds, including work with tiles and cardboard shapes, and paper folding and cutting for shapes to be made into models, gives children a basis on which spatial ability may develop.[1]

[1] Morton found that children with number forms had superior ability in mechanical arithmetic, 13 out of 17 were in the upper quartile of test results. See Number Forms and Arithmetical Ability in Children, by Dan M. Morton, *Brit. J. Educ. Psych.*, Vol. 6, Part I, pp. 58-73.

Fletcher found that only 1 child in 35 possessed number forms and they were of doubtful use in arithmetic. B. Fletcher, *Number Forms in Children* (M.Ed. thesis, University of Leeds, 1951)

Emotional Attitudes

Investigations show that the popularity of arithmetic as a school subject varies from age group to age group, from boys to girls, and from normal to dull pupils, but of course the success which pupils experience—and this is dependent on the way in which teaching methods are adapted to suit pupils—largely determines the pupils' attitudes towards the subject.

Burt[1] (in 1930) gave the following preference positions, in a list of fifteen school subjects, for boys and girls:

Age	7		10		13	
	Boys	Girls	Boys	Girls	Boys	Girls
	7/15	13/15	9/15	14/15	11/15	15/15

These figures in themselves reflect interesting sex differences, while the position 15/15 for girls aged 13 is an indication of the ineffectiveness and barrenness of appeal, as shown in the dislike of the subject by the pupils, of much of the arithmetic teaching to senior girls twenty-five years ago.

Further figures of preferences, obtained in 1936[2] from approximately 9,000 boys and girls between the ages of 10 and 14, show the following positions for arithmetic in the various age groups of boys and girls:

Age	10		11		12		13	
	Boys	Girls	Boys	Girls	Boys	Girls	Boys	Girls
	7/17	9/17	3/13	6/17	2/17	5/17	5/13	10/17

[1] *Primary School Report,* Appendix III, Memorandum on the Mental Characteristics of Children between the Ages of Seven and Eleven, by Cyril Burt, p. 278

[2] J. J. Shakespeare, An Enquiry into the Relative Popularity of School Subjects in Elementary Schools, *Brit. J. Educ. Psych.,* June 1936

What perhaps is most striking in this study is the separate figures given for bright and for dull pupils. For bright pupils arithmetic is high up on the list of preferences, while for dull pupils it is very low, an indictment of methods and curricula in arithmetic for less able pupils. Questioning of the pupils revealed that dislike of the subject was very largely associated with failure to obtain satisfactory results.

In a study by Freeman,[1] in 1946, of attitudes towards arithmetic, there is some evidence of an increase in popularity of the subject, occasioned no doubt by the lightening of the syllabus and the improvement in textbooks and teaching methods during the last 12 or 15 years. For each type of secondary school—grammar, commercial, technical and modern —the pattern of attitudes is very similar, with comparable percentages of pupils who like and dislike arithmetic in each of the four types of secondary schools. But again there is an emphasis of dislike of the subject by modern schoolgirls of 13+ to 14+. Obviously the form of arithmetic teaching at this stage requires greater modification than has hitherto been given in girls' secondary modern schools.

Temperament and Emotional Attitudes

So far in this analysis of factors underlying arithmetical ability we have dealt only with cognitive qualities, general and specific, as revealed in the pupil's intellectual power to understand, to remember and to apply what he has learnt in his computation and his problem solving, and with background experience that he brings to bear upon his understanding of number. But affective qualities such as those that enter into industry and persistence, into emotional attitudes towards the subject and even towards various parts of the subject, towards his teachers and towards his own success or failure in the subject, together with his temperament, all exert a very important influence on arithmetical ability.

[1] G. W. A. Freeman, *An Enquiry into the Attitudes of Secondary School Boys and Girls towards Arithmetic* (M.A. thesis, University of Birmingham, 1948)

In a study Barakat[1] found that character qualities correlate with mathematical attainments to the extent of 0·30 to 0·35. This, of course, is an overall correlation derived from the results of 300 children. With individual pupils emotional factors are at times more important than intellectual ones. This is borne out continuously in the study of cases of intelligent children backward at arithmetic, seen at the Remedial Education Centres in Birmingham and Brisbane. Barakat noted that emotional instability seems to correlate most highly with inaccuracy of computation and lack of industry with inefficiency in mathematical reasoning.

One of the major determinants of success in working sums is the degree to which the pupil can keep his mind persistently on the task in hand. The final step which gives the correct answer is dependent upon successful working of preceding steps, so that if there has been a decrease in sustained attention resulting in a single error, the whole calculation is wrong.

Numerous factors, singly or in combination, influence a pupil's ability to apply himself effectively during his arithmetic lessons. A lack of interest, continuous failure, the effects of censure, lack of any sense of achievement, disturbing thoughts or emotional conditions due to anxiety about himself or family matters, worry about work missed during absence, confusion arising from insecure knowledge (sometimes due to bad teaching), an impulsive manner—these and other emotional states all exert a more powerful influence on attainments in arithmetic than on those in any other school subject.

It would appear from research that some emotional conditions or attitudes derive partly from an innate basis while others are almost entirely the product of adverse environmental situations. There are some pupils whose mental 'make up' is such as continually to handicap them in arithmetic; their minds are apt to wander from a set train of ideas, the amount of wandering being dependent upon the continuity required in the activity and upon the amount of distraction, internal or

[1] M. K. Barakat, *Factors Underlying the Mathematical Abilities of Grammar School Pupils* (Ph.D. thesis, University of London, 1950). Summary in *Brit. J. Educ. Psych.*, November 1951, p. 239

external, at the time of the mental operation. Amongst these pupils are the highly suggestible (failure influences them unduly), the highly imaginative, the impulsive, the supersensitive and the nervous, a grouping which might not be either mutually exclusive or sufficiently inclusive. The difficulty experienced by many such pupils is that while working their sums they find it difficult to prevent outside stimuli from intervening. A loud noise, someone talking, a change in lighting, the effects of a past mental conflict, chance ideas on other topics, soon assume, momentarily, a major role and prevent the pupils from working with maximum efficiency. Naturally the degree of weakness in this group of pupils is dependent on level of general intelligence. The very bright child may offset considerably any weakness in emotional stability, and his inaccuracy may be of an intermittent rather than a permanent kind, shown more often in mechanical than in problem arithmetic. A digit may be added twice, a carrying figure omitted, a sum wrongly transcribed, a nought missed from the quotient—errors which can be minimised by careful checking when he arrives at an age when he will check his work.

Those emotional attitudes which derive very largely from environmental conditions include, firstly, those associated with physical states, and, secondly, those such as success, interest and confidence, or, alternatively, failure, apathy and loss of confidence.

It is a commonplace in psychology that physical states influence emotional states and intellectual output. Pupils who are physically fit can apply themselves, can concentrate and make sustained efforts, and the converse is true of those who are not physically fit. It is amongst pupils suffering from recurrent colds and catarrhal conditions, those recovering from the effects of infectious diseases, those requiring more sleep and rest, that one finds such a disproportionate number backward in arithmetic. For some of these there is no doubt that an improvement in their physical condition would produce an improvement in their arithmetical level.

But emotional attitudes produced by past experiences, particularly in the initial stages of arithmetic instruction, are even more potent than those having a physical basis. The successful pupil engages in his work and tackles new material with relative calm and confidence. He concentrates better as a result of his emotional poise, he applies himself better as a result of success and he persists longer when difficulties arise. On the other hand, the pupil who has met with more than the usual amount of failure and/or censure is decidedly more disturbed emotionally during arithmetic lessons and is more apprehensive of his ability.

The influence of emotional conditions on arithmetical ability was aptly illustrated by the remark of a head teacher who stated that one group of pupils in his school knew less arithmetic at the end of six months than when they began. Observation of the atmosphere in which the arithmetic lessons were conducted and an examination of the errors made in diagnostic tests were particularly revealing. During daily lessons the teacher was rarely quiet for more than a few minutes. Pupils were constantly being upbraided for careless work, untidy work, insufficient work, all lapses in calculation were censured, and there appeared to be an expectancy of 100 per cent. accuracy. Large crosses marked the sums wrong, small ticks marked those right. Never did one hear quiet, encouraging remarks. Under the strain of distraction and discouragement many pupils lost more than they gained in arithmetical attainment. The quietness, the encouragement, the tolerance, the effective individual help so necessary in arithmetic lessons were entirely absent. Although such an example as this is an uncommon one in most schools today, yet it throws into relief certain points relating to the teaching of arithmetic. It might be salutary for all teachers themselves to do a speed test each term, under some distraction, and then to bear in mind the nature and the number of the errors they have made when they deal with the inaccuracies of their pupils.

Sex Differences

Finally, one should make brief reference to sex differences in arithmetic. There is a sufficient volume of research evidence that there are no demonstrable differences in ability in mechanical arithmetic between boys and girls,[1] but that there is a very slight difference in favour of boys in problem arithmetic or arithmetical reasoning.[2] There have been studies which appeared to reveal a difference in computation in favour of boys, but later test surveys with unbiassed samples of both sexes and with adequate statistical treatment of results have not demonstrated any superiority in calculation on the part of boys.

Any differences between groups of boys and girls are probably due to differences in teaching and in attitudes towards the subject. With syllabuses better suited to children's capacities and interests, and improvements in the training of teachers in arithmetic teaching, particularly for the early school years, such differences disappear. In fact, with good teaching, there are in the upper grades of primary schools examples of classes in which there are more girls than boys in the upper quartile of the mechanical arithmetic scores.

The slight difference in problem arithmetic in the top 25 per cent. of pupils would appear to be related to an inherent sex difference of a temperamental kind, namely that boys are more inclined to work out problems from first principles and to accept the challenge of a new variant of a problem than girls who show strength in memorisation of types of problems and in application of set patterns of problem solving.

[1] Pauline Campbell, *Sex Differences in Intelligence, English and Arithmetic, as shown in a Set of Qualifying Tests* (B.Ed. thesis, University of Edinburgh)

[2] G. Macgregor, *Achievement Tests in the Primary School*, pp. 73-86. S.C.R.E., University of London Press

CHAPTER III

RESEARCH RESULTS IN ARITHMETIC

CHANGES IN PRIMARY SCHOOL SYLLABUS

THIS chapter deals briefly with the main changes and experimental findings that have influenced curricula and methods in arithmetic during the past three decades. A knowledge of the results of research and of enlightened classroom practice is of paramount importance to administrator and teacher alike for it may be the means of preventing a considerable amount of failure in arithmetic.

In the first place, the nature and the extent of the syllabus in arithmetic, particularly in primary schools, has in almost every community undergone drastic changes. As an example of this change we might compare part of a primary school arithmetic syllabus in 1930 with its revision in 1952.

1930 *Syllabus*	1952 *Syllabus*
First Year: Addition and subtraction to 10.	First year is a complete preparatory year without requirements of a formal kind.
Second Year: Addition and subtraction to 99.	Second Year: Addition and subtraction to 10.
Third Year: Addition and subtraction to 999. Multiplication and division by numbers to 6.	Third Year: Addition and subtraction to 99. No multiplication and division.
Fourth Year: Addition and subtraction to 10,000. Multiplication by two figures. Division by one figure.	Fourth Year: Addition and subtraction to 999. Multiplication by numbers to 6. Division by numbers to 6.

Now changes like this have been due to a number of forces. Experimental studies have caused us to modify considerably our interpretation of the theory of the transfer of training, so that we no longer subscribe to the view that a study of arithmetic improves a pupil's ability to reason and aids him to develop concentration and persistence. When the old transfer of training theory prevailed, syllabuses for upper classes were overloaded, and included all kinds of barren requirements such as unduly long calculations, artificial types of problems (tea mixing, baths, racing sums, etc.), compound interest, short methods (*e.g.* 17s. 10¼d. as a decimal of £1 mentally), and every conceivable rule of mensuration, usable or unusable.

Furthermore, educational psychologists and teachers have produced evidence on what children are capable of understanding and learning in arithmetic at different levels of age and intelligence.

One of the earliest of such investigations was that carried out in 1928 by the Committee of Seven[1] under the chairmanship of C. W. Washburne. Under their direction a comprehensive testing programme, which included both intelligence and arithmetic tests, was undertaken to find the mental age that was necessary for pupils to master and retain particular processes. The criterion used was that a process was understood if 75 per cent. of the pupils who gained satisfactory initial scores in a process or topic could still score 80 per cent. in the retention tests given six weeks later.

They found that many pupils were expected to master topics before they were mentally able to understand them. One example was long division by two figures, which ten-year-olds were expected to master but which, on the evidence of the tests, really required a mental age of twelve for success. A similar divergence between what was expected of children and what they could achieve was found in the case of addition and subtraction of fractions; often children were being asked to add or subtract unlike fractions long before they had had a chance of really understanding the various concepts underlying the addition and subtraction of fractions.

Naturally the findings of this Committee were not accepted

[1] First report published in *Elem. Sch. J.*, Vol. 27, pp. 59-665: When Should we Teach Arithmetic, by C. W. Washburne. Those interested in the findings of the Committee may consult the 38*th Year Book* of the National Society for the Study of Education, Chapter 16, Child Development and the Curriculum (University of Chicago Press, Chicago, Illinois).

without criticism[1] and subsequent research has resulted in some modification of their findings. For example, Curr,[2] investigating factors determining success in simple division, found that successful learning of a topic was not simply a matter of the age at which the topic was begun. *The level of I.Q. of children learning the topic and the effectiveness of their foundation knowledge in related number combinations were vital determinants of success in the topic.*

Those pupils who are mentally older, *i.e.* have a higher I.Q., do better than those with lower I.Q.; it was the children with higher I.Q.s who made better scores when topics were postponed in the Committee of Seven research. That is, while postponement is important, it is the level of intellectual maturity that matters most. Curr pointed out that there may be mental ages below which children may not be able to succeed with particular topics, but he might also have noted that in so far as difficult topics *are* postponed all children will be mentally older and hence will have a better chance of success with the topics.

However, it is safe to say that the Committee of Seven findings had widespread influence on both sides of the Atlantic in stimulating educationists to question the ages, mental and chronological, at which children were expected to master the various arithmetical processes. Furthermore, the Committee's statements have led to much worthwhile research in this field of determining the difficulty of different topics for children of various ages and intellectual levels.[3] For example, experiments with the teaching of long division have resulted in postponing more difficult types till later.[4]

[1] *See* The Values, Limitations and Applications of the Findings of the Committee of Seven, by C. W. Washburne, *J. Educ. Res.*, Vol. 29, pp. 344-54, and a Critique of the Committee of Seven's Recommendations on Grade Placement of Arithmetic Topics, by W. Brownell, *Elem. Sch. J.*, Vol. 38, pp. 495-508.

[2] W. Curr, Placement of Topics in Arithmetic, *Studies in Arithmetic*, Vol. 2, pp. 183-215 (S.C.R.E. Publication, University of London Press)

[3] Readiness and the Arithmetic Curriculum, *Elem. Sch. J.*, Vol. 38, pp. 495-508

[4] As an example see Relative Difficulty of Types of Examples in Division with Two-Figure Divisors, by L. J. Brueckner and H. O. Mellige, *J. Educ. Res.*, Vol. 33, pp. 401-414.

Thus there has been a trend in arithmetic syllabuses to postpone till later processes that experience has shown to be too difficult for many pupils at certain ages, and to limit considerably the size of the numbers that children are required to use and to understand. For example, multiplication and division are taught later, long division is started at least a year later in most syllabuses, and involved exercises combining all four rules in fractions have been replaced by smaller sums applied to concrete quantities. Many more everyday types of examples dealing with small numbers have been introduced and pupils in the primary school are less frequently required to work sums involving 5 or 6 digits.

Naturally, in the revised grade or age allotment of topics there are variations from area to area in what it is claimed children can understand and should be taught in the different grades of primary schools. For example, some schools introduce children of 8 or even 7+ to the idea of fractions ($\frac{1}{4}$ and $\frac{1}{2}$) through concrete experiences, while other schools postpone it entirely to 9+. But whatever the variations from one school system to another, there is widespread agreement in respect to approximately 90 per cent. of the topics and their age allocations.[1] And what is more important, in no country would syllabus requirements acceptable in 1926 or even 1936 be acceptable in 1956. Of course, we have little exact evidence of how much of the more extensive primary school syllabuses were really understood in 1926, but we do know that arithmetic was the bugbear of teacher and pupil alike and that a teacher's reputation and even his promotion depended upon obtaining good results in the terminal and final arithmetic tests. Few worried overmuch about the children's knowledge or skill in art, music, handicrafts or natural history.

No Decline in Standards

The lightening of the syllabus—so that children do less but understand what remains much better—has come in for severe

[1] See, for example, the recent survey of courses of study in primary school arithmetic in six Australian States. Duplicated report, Australian Council for Educational Research, Melbourne, 1953

criticism from 'the old brigade', who continue to repeat fallacious mental discipline arguments and who openly state that pupils' standards in calculation are lower now than they were twenty-five years ago, now that 'long tots', difficult multiplication and division of money sums, involved exercises in reduction and other such non-functional examples are no longer foisted on every child.

But in point of fact we have objective proof that computational accuracy has not declined. Results from Burt's standardised arithmetic tests, given in the years 1921-5 in various parts of England and repeated at least twenty years later, did not show, in the main, any decline in standards in the four rules. And from a more recent experiment in Australia comes similarly reassuring evidence. In 1931 and again in 1946 the Australian Council for Educational Research administered certain arithmetic tests to selected groups of children in particular grades in Queensland schools. These same tests were applied to a representative sample of Queensland pupils in 1952. Between these years, however, there have been changes in the curriculum. More particularly it has been lightened in content and in requirements of knowledge of certain processes in earlier grades. A comparison of the results of the tests in 1931 and in 1952 showed quite clearly 'that the 1952 Grade VII pupils attained a higher standard than did their counterparts of twenty years ago in mechanical and problem arithmetic as measured by the tests used'.[1]

The actual results were:

	1931 Mean	1952 Mean
Mechanical Arithmetic B	18·9	19·9
Problem Arithmetic B	16·8	18·2

These differences are statistically significant and are most unlikely to be due to chance. This finding provides a very strong justification for the changes that have been made.

[1] Department of Public Instruction, Research and Guidance Branch, Brisbane. Bulletin No. 7 *Research Findings in Arithmetic*

But curriculum changes in arithmetic could go further in some countries to make a place for social training, in which some British schools are weak.

Social Value of Arithmetic

Finally, arithmetic syllabuses in the schools of enlightened educational systems have undergone fairly close scrutiny in terms of their social value to the pupil. How much arithmetic do children really need for everyday life situations when they leave school at 15 or 16? Do particular topics in arithmetic really function in everyday life or are they artificial, useless and even misleading (as in sums on papering rooms or carpeting floors)? These and other questions have been persistently asked by those who believed that too much arithmetic and the wrong sort of arithmetic were still being taught in schools. Thus topics such as the home budget, weekly shopping expenditure, transport costs of a family, or, for older pupils, transport costs of a city, the running of a tuck shop, a school store, a bazaar or a school garden, post office arithmetic, problems dealing with time-tables and times involved in state and interstate travel, costs of decorations, furnishings and alterations to the home—these and a host of other topics all intimately related to life requirements have begun to oust the artificial and non-functional parts of the previously accepted arithmetic syllabuses. And results show that not only do pupils like this type of arithmetic better, but they learn it better too, for learning most often occurs with maximum efficiency when it is associated with real situations that engender both interest and understanding.

Sections and Individual Work

In almost every school class there is a sufficiently wide range in the arithmetical abilities of the pupils to warrant some form of internal class organisation by means of sections or groups, with individual help to weaker members, that will enable *all* children to make progress commensurate with their ability. Naturally this need is less in schools where numbers permit of classification into two or three streams, or where some form of ability grouping is used.

Some schools go so far as to make provision for arithmetic instruction throughout the school by means of organisation distinct from the register classes of the pupils. On the basis of a series of tests pupils are divided into arithmetic 'classes' or sets, and thus each set may contain children from a number of different register classes. This arrangement naturally means that all pupils must do arithmetic at the same hour in the school day, and it means a certain amount of movement to and from classrooms. It also means, or should mean, that (in order to keep sets as homogeneous as possible) at the end of the first term a minimum number of children, who have either made marked progress, or who still find the work in the set too difficult for them, should be transferred 'up' or 'down' to other sets. Although class teachers do not teach all of their own register pupils for arithmetic, yet the greater homogeneity of the group enables them to proceed at a pace suitable to all. Those who have tried this form of organisation and who have been able to check its success by objective measures are largely in favour of it. Of course, it does mean change, to which those concerned have to become accustomed, but teachers themselves indicate how beneficial this form of organisation is to the really bright children, who can go ahead, and to the slow learners, who can be given work, and taught at a pace, which suits them.

However, not all schools are attracted to this form of organisation, nor do numbers or physical conditions make it possible. In some classes, therefore, where there is a wide range of attainments, it might be necessary, if the bright children are not to be kept back and the slow ones are not to be overdriven,[1] to form sections based on the arithmetic attainments of the pupils. From wide experience I believe that two sections, one of the able and the other of the slower or less able pupils (although there may be the need to have a third) are all that a

[1] For a description of a similar form of organisation for English in a secondary modern school, see pp. 444-47 of *Backwardness in the Basic Subjects*, 3rd ed., by F. J. Schonell (Oliver and Boyd).

teacher can really manage effectively. It is doubtful if there is the need to have more than two sections, even if teachers could deal with more, where really good textbooks are used with a large range of finely graded examples. One secret of successful arithmetic instruction, and certainly a measure that minimises individual difficulties, is effective grading of steps in a process and the provision of an adequate number of finely graded examples on each step.

Sometimes it is useful to take the class as a whole for the teaching of new work, afterwards dividing it into sections of the brighter and the slower pupils in respect to the complete understanding of the rule. Section A may require a further demonstration of the new material, while Section B can start sooner and go further with the graded examples that follow the explanatory or teaching lesson.

But sections or groups, however well formed and skilfully handled, do not dispense with the need for individual help to children during almost every arithmetic lesson. Sometimes this help needs to be given to just one child who cannot understand a particular point. At other times there may be four or five slow ones who are still making errors in a newly demonstrated step or in an older one of which they are uncertain. A few minutes at the blackboard or round the table can often work wonders with such pupils.

UNDERSTANDING FOLLOWED BY PRACTICE

The newer trend in arithmetic teaching, based on research into children's difficulties and aimed at preventing failure, is to devote more time to enabling pupils to understand more effectively what they are learning before engaging in practice on the particular topic. In other words, the old inductive method of *telling* the rule, or showing the method to pupils and then letting them apply it more or less blindly through continuous practice, is being superseded (too slowly amongst some teachers) by the greater use of deductive methods, of putting before children experiences that will enable them to see the relationships and discover the rule for themselves.

A very simple example of this is found in the newer approach of letting pupils find out number relationships for themselves by the use of concrete materials. (See page 134). And a related example is the learning of the multiplication tables. Under the older methods children were presented with the table to be learnt, written on the blackboard or on a chart. All they had to do was memorise it. Those who failed simply had not worked hard enough and required more sing-song repetition or more homework. *The newer method is to allow every child to build up his own multiplication table from concrete material.* With young children the development of the 2, 3, 4 times tables is often preceded by practical work in the grouping of concrete objects (matches, beads) or in cutting out pictures of objects and then arranging them in twos, threes, etc, or in making drawings of objects in pairs, threes, fours etc. They then have a basis of meaningful understanding in which to frame their practice. As I shall indicate later (page 142), I believe that children should do this for every table as the occasion requires, and, at the appropriate point, make up the corresponding division table.

Introducing meaning into number usually results in greater transfer of training, when the basic arithmetical knowledge is applied to a variety of situations. Thiele[1] conducted an experiment in which two groups of pupils were compared in respect of the learning of the 100 basic addition facts. One group learnt them by repetition only; the other was enabled to understand the relationships between the addition facts and so were helped towards generalisation. The relationship-generalisation group showed superior transfer ability and led to Thiele's remark that 'strong evidence is presented in this study to support the faith of those who would make arithmetic less of a challenge to the pupil's memory and more of a challenge to his intelligence'.[2]

As a second example of this we might take the pupils'

[1] C. L. Thiele, *The Contribution of Generalisation to the Learning of Addition Facts.* Contributions to Education No. 763. (Teachers' College Columbia University, New York, 1935)

[2] Quoted on p. 286 of *Arithmetic in General Education*, by T. R. McConnell (The National Council of Teachers of Mathematics, 1941)

introduction to area. They may approach it in the following way. Draw this on a piece of squared paper:

How many squares 'big' is it?

Then in groups of four they may be asked to measure the tops of boxes which have been provided for the lesson. Their results are then written on the blackboard in this form:

	Length of box	*Width of box*
Group 1.	10 inches	4 inches
2.	8 inches	6 inches

All groups are then required to draw a plan of the top of the box they measured, and to divide it into squares so that they can find how many squares 'big' it is. By discussion the teacher can then establish the idea of square measure with its units of square inches, square feet and so on. From this the formulae can be framed by the children themselves. They will really understand that 'number of squares big' or the number of the same units of square measure of a surface constitutes its area. But more important, they will have a real idea of surface measurement.

The older teaching method was to demonstrate from a drawing the idea of length × breadth = area and to give children numerous examples to do in order to consolidate the rule. Often, of course, pupils did not really understand what they were doing and blithely multiplied feet by inches to get square inches (or they would, to please you, change the answer to square feet—surely that must be right!). A full hour's practical lesson, or even two lessons, naturally takes much longer than the old $a = l \times b$ approach, but it results in much fuller understanding and fewer 'meaningless' errors.

The value of this kind of approach is firmly based on research results which prove conclusively that children who have had such experience in which they first discover the number relationships for themselves—or the method or the rule involved, as the case may be—*followed by later practice or drill*, are in the main quicker and more accurate in their arithmetic than those who are merely shown the relationship, or told the method or rule, and then set to work examples without any practical activity and its subsequent deductive strength. It is obvious that this superiority results from the fact that pupils who have adequate practical work really see sense in what they are learning, because they discover the meanings and the relationships for themselves. They then know what they are committing to memory by drill and why it will be useful to them.

Everyday Applications of Arithmetic

Another major change in arithmetic teaching which has led to better understanding of the purpose of arithmetic, and to an increased liking for arithmetic by pupils, has been the trend to make provision for a much wider application of number to everyday life situations. This has been done not only by using improved types of examples, based on real life situations, and greatly improved textbooks, but also by devoting specific time in junior and senior classes to what are variously called 'number projects', 'centres of interest' and 'experience units'.

America, influenced by the pragmatic test that Dewey and his followers applied to school knowledge and methods, has been a leader in this analysis of items in arithmetic syllabuses in terms of their functional value for everyday life. Surveys and analyses of syllabuses and textbooks have demonstrated that whole sections of the accepted courses of study often had little value in daily life. Gradually arithmetic in many American schools has become increasingly centred round real problems and round the life situations of the pupils and their parents.

This approach to the teaching of arithmetic has allowed it to be linked with real experiences instead of being concerned, as hitherto, only with the formal matter of the classroom. Experience units and projects have done more than anything else to change pupils' attitudes towards arithmetic. Children have been enabled to see that arithmetic can be meaningful, that it can be interesting and that it is useful. Because the arithmetic of a project is connected with the immediate need of a group of learners, it is often pursued with much greater intellectual strength and purpose than if it had been merely an artificial classroom exercise.

In the past arithmetic was very formal and abstract, and the use of projects or experience units has been of inestimable value in demonstrating the social value of the subject. No teacher can afford to neglect project work in his arithmetic teaching. Those who maintain that there is no need for such 'new-fangled methods', that 'there isn't time' or that 'it won't teach children how to do arithmetic', do not understand the vital and all-pervading value of such experiences for children as a means both of discovering new arithmetical information and of applying old. If teachers do not occasionally use projects, however small, as a supplement to ordinary lessons, they are neglecting one of the most stimulating and effective learning devices of the century.

Examples of types of experience units for juniors and seniors are given by these titles:

Juniors

The Week's Shopping
A Post Office Project
How We Get Our Milk
How We Get Our Bread, etc.
Our School Shop
Our School Garden

Seniors

School Meals
A Gardening Project
A Home Furnishing Project
How People Learned to Tell the Time
The Cost of Our Health Service
The Family Budget
A Bank Project
A Post Office Project
Transport in the Community
A Travel Project

All projects should include, wherever possible, some searching for information on the part of the children themselves, some group work, some constructive activities and, if at all feasible, an excursion or visit outside the school in which children gain supplementary information about 'arithmetic in action'.[1]

Methods

During the past twenty-five years there has been an immense amount of research into methods in arithmetic, some of it conclusive, some of it merely suggestive, and an appreciable proportion of it almost useless because of the specificity of the experimental situation or the inadequacy of the statistical measures used.[2]

In addition to the two excellent studies[3] by the Scottish Council for Research in Education, the results of which have been summarised briefly by John Morrison in *The Teaching of Arithmetic* (University of London Press), those interested in research in arithmetic might consult the following:

> The Sixteenth Year Book of the National Council of Teachers of Mathematics, entitled *Arithmetic in General Education* (Bureau of Publications, Teachers' College, Columbia University, New York, 1941)
>
> *The Encyclopaedia of Educational Research*, ed. S. Monroe: Section on Arithmetic by G. M. Wilson, pp. 44-58. (Revised edition, The Macmillan Co., New York, 1950)
>
> Teaching Mathematics Grades I Through VI, *Review of Educational Research,* October 1942, October 1945, October 1948, October 1951. The *Review of Educational Research* is published by The American Educational Research Association, a Department of the National Education Association of the U.S.A., 1201 Sixteenth Street N.W., Washington 6, D.C.

[1] See *Modern Practices in the Elementary School*, by T. A. Hackett and E. W. Jacobson (Ginn, 1938) and *Guidance of Learning Activities*, by W. H. Burton (Appleton Century, 1944), Chapters 9 and 10.

[2] See, for example, an article which sounds a note of caution in *Arithmetic in General Education*, Chapter XIII—The Interpretation of Research, by Wm. A. Brownell and Foster E. Grossnickle.

[3] *Studies in Arithmetic*, Vols. 1 and 2 (University of London Press)

The Elementary School Journal has also had short summaries of arithmetic research from time to time.

The Teaching of Arithmetic, Fiftieth Year Book of the National Society for the Study of Education (University of Chicago Press, Chicago 37, Illinois, 1951)

In this section I shall make brief reference to findings of research on methods, the observance of which may prevent a certain number of difficulties arising for some children.

Methods in Addition. The Scottish Council for Research in Education found exceedingly small differences between pupils taught to add upwards and those taught to add downwards. American research has shown that upward addition leads to slightly greater efficiency. *Upward addition should therefore be taught first and later pupils should be encouraged to use downward addition as a check.*

Methods in Subtraction. Methods of subtraction have been the subject of more experimental investigations and reviews than any other topic in arithmetic, but before considering the trend of results from this research the reader should be acquainted with the various methods employed in different school systems.

Methods of Teaching Subtraction

There are in essence two methods of teaching subtraction, namely (1) the method of *decomposition* and (2) the method of *equal additions*. In *decomposition* the essential point is that tens are broken up or decomposed to enable 'borrowing' to be done. In *equal additions* one 10 or one 100 is given to the unit or the tens column of the subtrahend, and then one 10 or one 100 is paid back to the 10s or 100s. Consider the example

$$\begin{array}{r} {}^{5}\not{6}\ 1 \\ -\ 3\ 9 \\ \hline \end{array}$$

Using *decomposition* the pupil's mental steps would be: '9 from 1, I can't. Borrow one 10 from the 10s column. One 10 from six 10s leaves five 10s. 9 units from 11=2. *3 from 5=2*'

Using *equal additions* the pupil's mental steps would be:

$$\begin{array}{r} 6\ 1 \\ -\ 3\ 9 \\ \hline \end{array}$$

'9 from 1, I can't. Give one 10 to the units column. That makes 11 units. I must pay back one 10 to the 10s column. Three 10s and one 10 are four 10s. 9 units from 11=2. *4 from 6=2*'.

But there may be two variations of the way in which the pupil carries out the subtraction of the numbers, irrespective of the method he employs in doing the process. He may use a *subtractive* form, *i.e.* 11—9 or 9 from 11, as used in illustrations of the methods above. Alternatively, he may use an *additive* or *complementary* method, in which case his mental steps would be:

$$\begin{array}{r} 6\ 1 \\ -\ 3\ 9 \\ \hline \\ \hline \end{array}$$

Using the method of decomposition with additive or complementary subtraction:

9+?=11, or I must add 2 to 9 to make 11.
3+?=5, or I must add 2 to 3 to make 5.

Using the method of equal additions with additive or complementary subtraction:

9+?=11, or I must add 2 to 9 to make 11.
4+?=6, or I must add 2 to 4 to make 6.

It will be seen that the additive or complementary method of dealing with the numbers enables the child to make use of his knowledge of number relationships. In respect to 11, 2 is the complement of 9, and naturally the method would be facilitated by teaching the addition and subtraction relationship of all numbers, *e.g.*

2+9=11
9+2=11
11—2= 9
11—9= 2

Thus there are four common methods of subtraction:

(1) decomposition with subtractive calculation,

(2) decomposition with an additive or complementary calculation,

(3) equal additions with subtractive calculation,

(4) equal additions with additive or complementary calculation.

Both aspects of learning subtraction *i.e.* the process and the form of calculation of subtraction of the numbers, have been the subject of research. Most investigations have been engaged on comparing the methods of equal additions and decomposition but there is also experimental evidence on the respective merits and demerits of subtractive and additive methods of dealing with the number combinations.

Research Techniques used to Compare Methods

In the main research results on methods of subtraction have been obtained by using the experimental technique of *differential testing*, that is, applying specially prepared tests to two separate but representative groups of pupils equated as nearly as possible in mental age, I.Q. and chronological age. One of these groups has learnt a process or acquired certain information by one method, while the other has learnt the skill or acquired the knowledge by a second or different method. The test results from the two groups of pupils are considered to reveal differences in accuracy—or speed, or understanding, as the case may be—which may be ascribed to differences in the methods used. Of course the weakness is in the assumption that each method was equally well or badly taught by the teachers of the pupils used in the experiment.

This kind of experimental technique was used by Johnson and by Murray[1] in comparing methods of subtraction. Johnson equated his group in terms of I.Q., mental age and level of basic arithmetic attainments. Murray's research involved pupils in 55 different schools—of which 24 used equal addition,

[1] See pp. 21-70 of *Studies in Arithmetic*, Vol. 2, on The Relative Merits of Methods of Teaching Subtraction, by John Murray. Publication of the Scottish Council for Research in Education, University of London Press

19 decomposition and 12 complementary—and it related to two age groups, namely 8-9 years (*i.e.* beginners with subtraction) and 10-11 years (*i.e.* with some years of experience of subtraction). All were given tests at a fixed time during a selected week and the results were based on a comparison of speed and accuracy scores for the various methods. The statistical significance of the differences between the methods was checked by four different statistical formulae.

There have been a few research studies which used the experimental technique of *control groups*. This involves the equating, as far as possible, of groups of children who have not had any experiences of subtraction methods as such, in terms of I.Q., mental age, chronological age and level of early attainments in number.[1] Arrangements are then made to teach each group of pupils by a different method of subtraction. After a certain period has elapsed further tests are given to determine the efficiency of each particular method.

Most of the studies undertaken have used the two criteria of accuracy and speed in judging the efficiency of the various methods, and it should also be noted that more investigations have been concerned with the level of efficiency achieved after a number of years by each of the methods than with the efficiency and rate with which children learn subtraction by each of the different methods.

Results of Investigations

Almost all research results from Ballard's early work in 1914 to the later investigations of Johnson (1938)[2] and Murray (1941)[3] *favour the method of equal additions or carrying method*

[1] Details of the preparation for, and the methods employed in equating the groups and the actual conduct of an experiment of this kind involving a large number of children in different schools are to be found in *Meaningful v. Mechanical Learning*.

[2] J. T. Johnson, *The Relative Merits of Three Methods of Subtraction: An Experimental Comparison of the Decomposition Method of Subtraction with the Equal Additions Method and the Austrian Method.* Teachers' College Contributions to Education No. 738, Teachers' College, Columbia University, 1938

[3] John Murray, The Relative Merits of Methods of Teaching Subtraction. *Studies in Arithmetic*, Vol. 2, pp. 27-70. Scottish Council for Research in Education, University of London Press, 1941

as compared with the decomposition or borrowing method. Murray's investigation in Scotland covered groups of children between the ages of 8 and 9 years (in 55 schools) and 10 and 11 years (in 54 different schools) in respect to both accuracy and speed and showed that the decomposition method was decidedly inferior to the equal additions method with both groups of children and for both speed and accuracy of subtraction.[1] But results from studies of the subtractive versus the additive or complementary methods of dealing with subtraction combinations have not yielded the same clear-cut conclusions. Some results seem to favour a subtractive method while others lend support to an additive or complementary method. It is argued that a complementary method is a logical development of information already known through addition—that it is more logical to say $2+?=11$ rather than $11-2=?$. It does not necessarily follow, however, that if the child knows $2+9=11$ then he will naturally be able to transfer to $2+?=11$, although, of course, all cross relationships between pairs of number combinations should be stressed at the time of teaching.

Brownell and Moser's Experiment

This experiment involved 1400 third grade children enrolled in 41 classes in schools of North Carolina, none of whom had had any experience in borrowing in subtraction. These were then divided into three groups, Centres A, B and C. The difference between the classes was that in *Centre A* grades 1 and 2 received a considerable amount of systematic work in arithmetic with an emphasis upon meaningful experience; in *Centre B* there was a small amount of meaningful arithmetic teaching in the early grades, and in *Centre C* the arithmetic teaching to classes of children in grades 1 and 2 was small in amount and conducted mainly along formal lines. The children in each of the three centres were then grouped so as to provide

[1] Those who wish to consult summaries of the research done on methods of subtraction should read *Studies in Arithmetic* (1941), Vol. 2, pp. 24-43 and *Meaningful v. Mechanical Learning. A Study in Grade III Subtraction* (Duke University Press, 1949), pp. 3-22. Other summarised material is available in *Review of Educational Research,* Vol. 15 (1945), Vol. 18 (1948), Vol. 20 (1951), Vol. 23 (1954).

four experimental sections. Half of the classes then *learned to borrow by decomposition* and the other half *by equal additions*, and each half was divided again so that one section of the pupils learned their subtraction *in a meaningful way*, while the other section learned it *in a mechanical rule-of-thumb manner*. Thus there were four experimental sections of pupils:

(*a*) learning to subtract by decomposition with meaningful explanation;

(*b*) learning to subtract by decomposition in a mechanical way;

(*c*) learning to subtract by equal addition, with emphasis on meaningful explanation;

(*d*) learning to subtract by equal addition in a mechanical way.

The experiment involved equalising the sections in all centres in terms of accuracy of scores on a pre-test.

In all centres there were

(*a*) *a pre-experimental period* when all teachers helped pupils to gain mastery of the simple subtraction facts, taught them to subtract without borrowing of 2- and 3-place numbers and also to consolidate their addition knowledge with and without carrying with 2- and 3-place numbers;

(*b*) *an experimental period*, which lasted three school weeks, during which teachers taught the decomposition and equal additions methods in the ways indicated above to the particular sections;

(*c*) *a post-experimental period*, which covered six weeks, when no additional instruction was given, and practice was limited to the normal amount that occurred through the textbooks.

At the end of (*c*) a test was administered to all sections. The tests were accompanied by interviews for all children in Centres A and C.

The results[1] from this extensive experiment, though in the main favouring the equal addition method of subtraction, indicated that it was more quickly and successfully learnt 'in the case of children with relatively rich backgrounds of meaningful arithmetic'. There was ample evidence from the interviews with children and from the diaries of the teachers participating in the experiment to show that the equal addition method was more difficult to explain to children. This was mainly due to the fact that it involves a new principle, namely that the relative values of numbers are not changed if we add the same amount to each. In an equal addition method, pupils require careful teaching to help them realise the need to alter not only minuend but also subtrahend. The experiment did point to the value of building up for children a background of meaning in arithmetic if they are to succeed in later stages. However, it would seem that the findings in no way shake the previously established superiority of the equal addition method over the decomposition for both speed and accuracy. It has always been realised that the equal addition method requires more skilful teaching, but once it has been acquired—and it can be acquired by children of all intellectual levels—it results in superior subtraction ability. While agreeing with the authors of this excellent study upon the value of developing in children an understanding of what they are doing in arithmetic, and of its cumulative effect, we would point out that this understanding should come through actual experience and not merely through rational explanation by the teacher.

There is some evidence to show that with children of only average intelligence we can over-emphasise the rational explanation approach and hold up to some extent the quick and effective assimilation of a method in a mechanical, semi-automatic way. With children who are not so quick at grasping arithmetical explanations, it is advisable to provide opportunities for them to 'get their sums right' by the application of rule-of-thumb methods. There are hundreds of thousands of people

[1] For a detailed consideration of them see *Meaningful v. Mechanical Learning. A Study in Grade III Subtraction* (Duke University Press, 1949), Chapters III and IV, pp. 150-59.

who today still do multiplication of decimals or square root by such methods, and without any loss of efficiency.

This carefully planned study also afforded evidence on the use of crutch figures, *e.g.*

decomposition	equal addition
6	
$\not{7}\;\;{}^{1}2$	$7\;\;{}^{1}2$
$5\;\;\;6$	$6\not{5}\;\;\;6$
——	——

Analysis of children's results and observations by teachers showed that crutches enabled children to understand a method more quickly and to apply it more effectively. Furthermore, they were not hampered on gaining the ability to subtract without the use of crutches. This is further confirmation of what I have continuously advocated as a result of my studies of children who fail in arithmetic: that if children can get their sums right by using crutches let them. They will discard such aids when they no longer require them.

Methods in Short Division

There is research evidence to show that in short division the form of setting out which places the quotient on top of the line, *e.g.* $6\overline{)189}$, is preferable to the form $6)\underline{189}$, because children can more easily make the change from short division to long division. In fact, our first introduction to long division can be the working out in long division form of examples previously solved by short division methods. If the first form of setting out is used, there is no need to make any change when the class is introduced to long division.

Use of Crutches in the Four Processes

The use of crutches, or small supplementary figures introduced by pupils (or teachers) for demonstration during the learning or later consolidation of basic processes in arithmetic, is from time to time a matter of controversy amongst practising teachers. Most recommend them, some view them with disfavour, while a few (among whom are the theorists) strongly condemn their use.

In the main they are favoured by most teachers, as enquiries showed in the arithmetic studies made by the Scottish Council for Research in Education.[1] Scottish teachers tended to allow children the use of crutch figures, particularly in the early stages of instruction, and then to discourage it later. The crutch in subtraction and division seems to be more needed than in addition and multiplication and hence persists longer, particularly among slower-learning pupils.

Opposition to the use of crutches has centred round two points. The first of these is that they are not necessary, but analysis of errors and questioning of pupils show that this is not so; almost all pupils need crutches in the early stages. The second reason advanced against the use of crutches is that once used they tend to persist. Analysis of children's working habits tends to show that this also is incorrect. Children in general (unless they are very slow learners) tend to drop crutches once they have acquired sufficient facility in the process.

Brownell and Moser's subtraction study gives evidence[2] that in learning subtraction children actually need crutches to facilitate the learning of borrowing. It was evident from their data that crutches could 'be discarded without too much trouble in the case of most children'.

The present trend is to allow children to use crutches so long as they have the need for them. The discerning teacher will, of course, know when to suggest to children that they may try to do without them, and to give praise when crutches are dropped, but obviously it is not advantageous to drop crutches if as a result inaccuracy increases.

[1] *Studies in Arithmetic*, Vol. 1, pp. 20-26. S.C.R.E. University of London Press, 1939

[2] *Meaningful v. Mechanical Learning: A Study in Grade III Subtraction*, by William A. Brownell and Harold E. Moser (Duke University Press, Durham, North Carolina, 1949)

CHAPTER IV

BACKWARDNESS IN ARITHMETIC

A KNOWLEDGE of the causes of backwardness in arithmetic is valuable to teachers not only from a remedial but also from a preventive standpoint. In arithmetic the motto 'Forewarned is forearmed' is doubly significant in the early stages of teaching, for much can be done to prevent initial errors and ensure success if one is aware of possible pitfalls.

Backwardness in arithmetic, as in other elementary school subjects, is usually due to a plurality of causes. The clear-cut case of backwardness which can be ascribed to a single cause is comparatively rare; the complex case which involves several causal factors is of common occurrence. We should therefore be prepared to find in most pupils backward in arithmetic several causal determinants of the paucity of their arithmetical attainments. For convenience of discussion, in the following sections causes are considered separately under each of three headings:

A. environmental: within the home and within the school,
B. intellectual,
C. emotional.

A. ENVIRONMENTAL CAUSES OF BACKWARDNESS IN ARITHMETIC

From the outset it should be realised that arithmetic is a particularly difficult and abstract subject. Adults who have become absolutely automatic in their manipulation of addition, subtraction, multiplication and division facts sometimes forget that the young pupil is far from the stage of automatic accuracy. Most young children are puzzled by the arbitrariness and abstractness of the whole process of number, and it is only when they have had a sufficiently varied and comprehensive experience with the concrete that some understanding of number is developed. Initially the child builds up his elementary ideas of number through the actual handling of objects. He first realises that one more thing than one makes two things, but he remains on this level for a considerable time and although he may use other numbers he has no real understanding of their function. Gradually he extends the sphere of his understanding through common everyday situations in which numbers are used, through games and through counting.

Counting is the basis of early number work and if the pupil is to understand unit values and group values he must have the opportunity for much counting with different kinds of material. Although this early experience in number is important for most pupils if they are to bridge the gulf between the concrete and the abstract, it is essential to all dull and backward pupils if they are to make any progress in arithmetic. In so far as their mental age is below normal compared with others of the same chronological age, they require prolonged and intensified activity in concrete number situations before any attempt is made with formal work.

Two causes of backwardness in arithmetic are thus apparent: namely lack of opportunity to acquire the requisite early number experience through handling and dealing with the concrete; and commencement of formal or abstract number work before the child has reached a mental level necessary for understanding relationships in an abstract medium.[1]

(1) *Paucity of Pre-School Experience*

For children whose out-of-school life is limited and narrow, who have had little chance of counting, comparing, contrasting, measuring, weighing and sharing, and who have had little opportunity of seeing number applied to real-life situations, it is necessary for the school to provide compensation for this limitation in their pre-school experiences. This can be, and is,

[1] For a very useful supplement to this section the reader is referred to *A Background to Primary School Mathematics*, Chapters I-VIII, L. D. Adams (Oxford University Press, 1953)

done in modern infant schools by allowing such children to engage in numerous occupations that will give them the correct attitude towards number and the knowledge of fundamental ideas necessary to start formal work in the four rules. These occupations include movement with toys, building with blocks, use of form boards, counting with all sorts of materials in different shapes and forms, playing with scales involving the weighing of different materials, pouring water into vessels of varying sizes, doing simple woodwork, playing at shops, dairies, post offices and so on.

There are many such activities, but care should be taken to see that they all directly bear upon the formation of early number ideas. Infant schools where formal work in number is postponed and where this kind of activity curriculum is substituted for the first six, nine or twelve months, according to the needs of the child, find that superior results are obtained when formal number is begun at this later age.

(2) *Too Early Commencement of Number with Dull Pupils*

The same treatment applies to dull pupils except that there is a need to continue the activity work longer. It is obviously uneducational that children with mental ages of $3\frac{1}{2}$ to $4\frac{1}{2}$ (though of chronological ages 5 to 6 years) should be required to begin formal number as soon as they enter the infant school. It should be realised that 'under present conditions many children at five are not mature enough to be taught anything except the names of the numbers. They should be placed in an environment where it is possible to work out their own salvation.'[1] If this were done there would be less failure and confusion and fewer emotional barriers created in the early stages of arithmetic teaching.

(3) *Other Home Influences*

The child who, not over-robust in health, gets insufficient sleep and perhaps insufficient food of a nourishing kind has

[1] M. Drummond, *The Psychology and Teaching of Number*, 3rd impression (Harrap), p. 17

neither the mental energy nor the power of concentration to maintain a consistent level of accuracy in an arithmetic lesson lasting forty, forty-five or even fifty minutes. Like the child who works early in the morning or late at night he soon fatigues and is easily distracted from his work, so that the mastery of new steps and the reproduction of old ones are often seriously affected.

For these pupils an enquiry into home conditions will often produce better results, particularly where hours of sleep are increased, than any actual individual assistance during arithmetic lessons. Furthermore, there is evidence that the arithmetic lesson for young pupils and for dull pupils is often too long. The degree of inaccuracy, produced partly by boredom, partly by physical fatigue, is often so great after twenty-five minutes that it would be much better to have, with the younger and the duller arithmeticians in a school, two twenty or twenty-five minute periods a day than a single one of thirty-five or forty minutes.

(4) *Absence from School*

Absence from school, whether intermittent or prolonged, is one of the most important causes of disability in arithmetic. For progress in arithmetic is like ascending a staircase; ascent to a new step is dependent upon the previous one, and if too many steps are missing, further progress is impossible. Furthermore, arithmetic is more susceptible to the influence of absences than any other school subject, for, whereas a child who has mastered the mechanics of reading can continue with his practice in out-of-school hours, this does not apply to arithmetic in which new types and new steps are so numerous. Systematic and regular practice with graded examples, so necessary to automatise past steps and to consolidate new ones, is usually obtained only under classroom conditions. Some of the most pronounced cases of retardation in arithmetic in the junior school are pupils who, as a result of prolonged, or of numerous short spells of absence, have had insufficient practice in some operation or no instruction at all in certain essential steps.

Use of the Diagnostic Tests[1] revealed pupils whose weakness in subtraction or in division was due to confusion in the early steps, which resulted from ineffective treatment after absences. It is not only that the pupil actually misses certain work, but that consequent failure and loss of confidence play their part in accentuating the effects of absence. Teachers should not fail to realise the feeling of dismay that absence from arithmetic lessons creates in some children. Adolescents to whom I have spoken can recall the loss of confidence that followed absence 'when two new kinds of sums were taught'. With many children, absent when new arithmetic material has been presented, there is need for definite individual work of a skilful kind to convince them that they can easily learn the new work and overcome their apparent handicap. The usual scanty explanations are insufficient.

(5) *Discontinuity*

(*a*) *Discontinuity between infant and junior departments.*—This is an accentuating factor in the backwardness of some pupils. The somewhat backward child, who is still doing his number work largely through the use of concrete material, apparatus, games and the use of props, and who is unfortunate enough to be placed in a class in a junior school where all such aids are missing and where the work is almost completely formalised, mechanical and uninteresting, can soon develop into an apparently stupid arithmetician. It is a misguided practice that deprives pupils of 7+ and 8+, particularly if they are not very bright, of apparatus and props as soon as they enter the junior school. Not a few of the dull ones require concrete material to help them with sums up to their tenth or eleventh year. Most children will use counters, dots and fingers only so long as they have a need for them. The aim is to get the sums right, and if children cannot do this without the use of props then their use should be continued, for the success achieved in getting a sum right is the vital part of the whole lesson and the factor which will best ensure the correct repetition of the same

[1] *Diagnostic Arithmetic Tests*, F. J. Schonell (Oliver and Boyd)

processes on a future occasion. No one prevents the adult from looking up forms of verbs or translations of words when he is learning a foreign language; he hopes to render the necessary associations automatic through correct usage. Similarly with the child correct usage in initial stages is all-important. Prevent the use of aids that are essential to this and a confusion is engendered that inhibits normal expression of mental powers.

Miss Renwick, in discussing the need for the concrete, goes so far as to say that even in the senior school 'a box of pieces of coloured cardboard could easily be prepared by the child and each pupil could conveniently keep his own supply of counters in readiness for his experiments with number'.[1]

(*b*) *Discontinuity between school and school or area and area.*— The pupil who moves from school to school or from area to area where methods of doing similar processes differ is likely to suffer from confusion if he experiences a second method in a fundamental operation before he has successfully mastered the first. No doubt variety and freedom in teaching are desirable, but in certain respects arithmetic is the subject least suited to diversity of method. For example, it has been proved beyond a shadow of doubt that the equal addition method of teaching subtraction results not only in greater accuracy but in greater speed as well. If this is the case, then let us all agree to teach subtraction by this method; the philosophic arguments of explanation should not deter us from the practical issues of the teaching problem. Similarly, with other methods and with the age levels at which certain processes are best taught, there is reliable evidence upon which uniformity of procedure should be based. Unless this uniformity is in operation from area to area backwardness in arithmetic will increase, not decrease, and cases such as the following will become more common. Bessie was just beginning to learn compound multiplication and had been taught to multiply from the right. Before she had had sufficient practice to master the work she was transferred to a school where the pupils multiplied from the left. Although the new method

[1] E. M. Renwick, *The Case against Arithmetic—A Teacher's Evidence* (Simpkin Marshall, 1935), p. 117

was explained several times she continued to flounder for several weeks, making errors like these:

35	35	35
18	18	18
2800	280	350
35	35	280
2835	315	3150

The nature of the errors reveals the complete confusion that existed in the child's mind with regard to the position of the figures.

In conclusion, it would not be overstressing the point to advocate that there should be a greater measure of centralisation of suggestions concerning the major principles of methods in arithmetic. Even where this uniformity is observed with regard to methods used and ages at which particular processes are most effectively taught to pupils of different intellectual calibres, there is adequate opportunity for individual variation in selection of examples, application to everyday situations, practical work, use of concrete material, use of games and interesting drill methods.

(*c*) *Too rapid promotion.* It sometimes happens that a child, particularly bright on the verbal side but perhaps only average in arithmetical attainments, 'skips' a class. This is right provided care is taken to link up the pupil's arithmetic knowledge from one class to the other and to ensure that he obtains adequate teaching and necessary practice in the arithmetic units that he would have done in the 'skipped' class. Amongst my records are not a few cases of retardation or relative backwardness in arithmetic in comparatively bright pupils, where the original causal factor appeared to be a too rapid promotion in the subject. The possible development of this condition is excluded in a school where cross-classification or arithmetic sets are used.

(*d*) *Lack of correspondence in syllabuses from school to school.* Where there is lack of correspondence in actual syllabus content from school to school pupils who transfer from one school to another are apt to miss vital units of work. The marked backwardness that some of these pupils exhibit after attendance at three or four different schools in the course of two years is further evidence that greater uniformity of procedure in sequence of, and age levels for, teaching the various arithmetical processes would decrease the amount of backwardness in arithmetic.

(6) *Teaching Methods*

Investigation with pupils backward in arithmetic shows that faulty teaching methods are contributory factors in the production of disability in arithmetic. One headmaster of a junior school is emphatic that 'much backwardness in arithmetic is induced backwardness, that is, created during the child's school career'. Of the attitudes and methods which are likely to contribute to or accentuate impoverished standards in arithmetic the following seem to be the most potent:

(*a*) *Over-explanation of processes with duller pupils.* There are some pupils, mainly the independent enquiring ones of supernormal intelligence, who must have, and who thrive on, explanations in arithmetic, but there are few pupils in 'B' or 'C' classes who require much explanation. What they require to know is how to get the sums right, and when they have learnt the method so thoroughly that the possibilities of getting the particular type of sums wrong are only the ordinary ones due to chance, then explanations might be attempted. Although most adults can divide one fraction by another or calculate square root, it is doubtful if more than 25 per cent. of them can explain their methods of working. Why then should we burden children with unnecessary explanation in arithmetic?

A similar observation might be made regarding practical work. Sometimes the degree of correspondence between supposed and actual clarification of a process by means of practical exercises is not very marked. We find pupils cutting out papers and pasting them in position without any conception of which principle is being demonstrated—the activity simply becomes one of paper-cutting. This does not imply that practical work in arithmetic is of questionable value—on the contrary it is an absolute necessity for dull pupils and for those specifically backward in arithmetic—but it does imply that practical exercises should be such that they really help the child to understand the process and consequently to get his sums right.

(*b*) *Over-emphasis of mechanical work.* Related to the last point is that of excessive mechanical work in arithmetic. Too much attention to purely mechanical exercises produces, particularly amongst dull children, an artificial division between arithmetic in school and arithmetic in everyday situations. 'Constant drill in the four rules, drill for its own sake, leads the children, especially if they are generally dull and backward in intelligence, to regard the four processes as four separate and distinct ideas entirely unrelated to one another. It is highly important that the problem or application aspect of number should be equally emphasised with children who are backward in arithmetic, since the dull mechanical work does in many cases increase their dislike of a subject that appears to them to be so useless.'[1]

(*c*) *A 'too-extensive' syllabus.* Arithmetic is a subject which has appealed to teachers, curriculum makers and textbook writers alike on account of its objectivity. Definite units of work can be selected, taught, applied and marked along clear-cut unequivocal lines. Furthermore, there still lingers the influence of a faulty faculty psychology which advocated that arithmetic teaches accuracy, trains in reasoning and encourages concentration. For these reasons arithmetic has tended to dominate the elementary school curriculum, with the result that too much arithmetic or unsuitable arithmetic is sometimes taught. But of recent years improvement has taken place and pupils are no longer required to grapple with cube root, compound interest, practice by aliquot parts, compound proportion, and complex problems of the type in which they had to find how soon a bath of a certain capacity would be filled if it had five taps and three outlet pipes each pouring

[1] E. Wheeler, *An Investigation into Backwardness in Arithmetic amongst London Elementary School Children* (M.A. thesis, University of London), p. 39

in or emptying, as the case might be, so much water per minute and all in operation at the same time. The curriculum for 'A' and 'B' pupils has been adjusted to some extent, but for less able pupils the work set is often beyond their abilities and their needs. Much of the backwardness in arithmetic amongst duller pupils would disappear if the curriculum were based on recognition of the fact that over 80 per cent. of the problems with which adults have to deal in everyday life involve only the four fundamental processes with numbers under 100, fractions —$\frac{1}{2}$, $\frac{3}{4}$, $\frac{1}{4}$, $\frac{1}{3}$—and percentages. Nearly 90 per cent. of the arithmetic is in connection with shopping.

But it is from the nature of the examples employed as well as from the syllabus that backwardness can be induced. Too often the pupil is asked to work exercises such as 96 tons 15 cwt. 3 qrs. 18 lb.$\times$74, 726826$\div$764, £361 : 18 : 9$\frac{1}{2}\times$96 when more sums of a simpler kind, like those actually experienced in life, would form a better preparation for life.

(*d*) *Commencing a new step before the previous one is mastered.* Backwardness is in part due to the practice of allowing pupils to begin a new process or step before they have mastered preceding ones. For example, it is unsound to introduce a pupil to the difficulties of 'carrying' in addition or 'borrowing' in subtraction before he has attained a high degree of efficiency in the 100 basic addition and subtraction facts. The first difficulty of inaccuracy in the fundamental combinations only makes for confusion when the second and greater difficulties are experienced. There should be more consideration of individual levels reached in arithmetic and more consideration of the mental levels at which children are normally ready for particular processes.

To achieve the first aim the arithmetic lesson might be completely individualised; this is done where the class is small or where there is a very wide range of arithmetical attainments. But a measure of success is obtained where sections within the class or arithmetic sets are used.

The second point involves more research into arithmetical abilities amongst elementary school pupils, but suggestive results on ages at which different processes should be begun have been obtained from an American investigation. 'The experiments show unmistakably that some of the topics of the school curriculum are commonly taught at points in children's growth which foredoom many to failure.'[1]

(*e*) *Bad grading of examples and an endeavour to teach two similar but not identical types of example in the same lesson.* These two aspects of arithmetic instruction are accentuating factors in backwardness. Careful grading of examples is essential to progress in arithmetic, yet one finds at times that after a new step has been taught insufficient simple examples are given to consolidate thoroughly the fresh knowledge. When a new step has been taken with a class it is advisable to give fifteen or twenty easy examples, each increasing very slightly in difficulty. As continued initial success is the dominant factor in enabling pupils to grasp the essentials of a new step, computational difficulties should be minimised in the early exercises, thereby allowing pupils to devote full attention to the method involved. Backwardness is produced when, with each new type of sum, the teacher gives only four or five simple examples and then plunges the pupils into relatively difficult variations—the brighter children succeed, the duller ones invariably flounder. There should always be a reasonable time interval between the teaching of new steps in a process.

Teaching similar but somewhat different types of examples in the same lesson is a procedure which confuses many rather dull children. For example, a class of pupils aged 10 to 11 years were taught in the same lesson two easy types of proportionate division, namely:

(*a*) Divide 10s. between 2 girls so that one has 3s. 6d. more than the other.

(*b*) Divide £20 between 2 boys so that one has 4 times as much as the other.

Insufficient examples were given to clinch type (*a*) before type (*b*) was begun, with the result that when miscellaneous examples were being worked the two types were confused. Thus examples such as:

[1] C. Washburne, *Adjusting the School to the Child* (World Book Co.), p. 39

Divide 144 nuts between Tom and Harry so that Tom shall have 24 more than Harry

would be solved by dividing 144 by 24.

B. Intellectual Causes of Backwardness in Arithmetic

(1) *Deficiency in General Intelligence*

The most obvious intellectual cause of disability in arithmetic is a defect in general intelligence. Arithmetic involves the use of symbols and, in so far as it is an abstract study making use of these symbols, it demands a considerable degree of general intelligence to succeed in it. Naturally the degree of general intelligence required is less when the examples are simple or when they are put in a mechanical form such as 40×8, but where they involve a complex set of relationships they demand a considerable degree of general intelligence. Thus a comparatively dull pupil may succeed with simple mechanical arithmetic but may fail hopelessly with relatively harder problem arithmetic. We have already indicated that general intelligence is the ability

(*a*) to see relevant relationships between items of knowledge;

(*b*) to educe correlates from these relationships, or, to put it in everyday language, to apply the relationships to new but similar situations.

Now arithmetic is saturated with relationships. For example, between the two numbers 6 and 2 numerous relationships may be perceived. Thus:

X_1 6×2
X_2 $6 \div 2$
X_3 $6 - 2$
X_4 $6 + 2$
X_5 2 is ? of 6
X_6 6 is ? times as great as 2.

These are all relationships perceived on the basis of the given fundaments, or items of knowledge. The second step of educing a correlate, demands greater general intelligence, that is, to give the answers, in this case 12, 3, 4, 8, $\frac{1}{3}$, 3.

All kinds of relationships may be perceived between items of knowledge but only those relevant to the situation in hand are of any use at a particular time. The relationships cited and the correlates educed in the above example are, however, comparatively simple. In such an example as the following they are considerably more complex:

> Three boys agree to divide some marbles so that the first shall have 20 more than the second and 30 more than the third. The number of marbles to be shared is 112. How many does each receive?

It will be apparent from the foregoing very brief discussion that lack of general intelligence will account for some backwardness in arithmetic, particularly in problem-solving, in which the perception of relationships demands not only memory but innate intellectual power.

(2) *Weak Memory for Numbers*

A defect in memory for numbers either immediate or delayed, sometimes both, is a common weakness of the backward arithmetician. It appears to be due to a combination of factors, chief of which are lack of interest in arithmetic, lack of confidence, and an innate deficiency in remembering numbers and number facts. The weakness shows itself in an inability to recall a sequence of numbers correctly—figures are omitted or transposed—so that often the pupil is most backward in oral or mental arithmetic. Sometimes this appears to arise from a definite weakness in visual imagery, that is, the pupil is unable to recall figures in his mind's eye. Thus in such an example as '39 horses cost £12 each. What was the total cost?' the pupil cannot see $\begin{array}{r}39\\ \times 12\\ \hline\end{array}$ set out on an imaginary blackboard.

It was noticeable that nearly all pupils weak in memory for

numbers failed with items like these (Nos. 35, 36 in Test 12, Diagnostic Arithmetic Tests[1]):

> Jack has to travel 100 yards along a straight road to school. He goes half way and then goes 25 yards along a side street and back to fetch a friend. How far does he walk to school?
>
> A box is 6 inches long, 6 inches wide, 6 inches deep. How much string will I need to tie it up if the string goes round the box twice (once each way) and I use 3 inches for the knot?

Experimental work shows that powers of visual imagery amongst children can be strengthened by practice—encouraging them to close their eyes and picture things before them.

The pupil who has a weak memory for numbers is prone to rely upon props and temporary aids. He makes constant reference to tables, or can only recall a particular unit in a multiplication table if he goes through the entire table, or must actually put in his sums the carrying and borrowing figures. Hence his arithmetic is marked by a disproportionate number of errors involving the omission of figures in addition, in quotients, and in borrowing and carrying.

(3) *Weakness in Concentration*

Allied with a weakness in memory for numbers is a certain inefficiency in concentration or attention. Here again the cause may be specific, arising from early failure, dislike of the subject, or too difficult or uninteresting material. There are some pupils who make foolish errors in their written arithmetic because of breaks in attention, but who do considerably better in oral arithmetic, particularly if the questions are attractively framed. On the other hand there are pupils for whom the repeated lapses in concentration have either a physical source or a psychological origin or in some cases a combination of both. The highly imaginative child or the pupil who is unwell or who suffers from the effects of semi-choreic instability, badly inflamed tonsils, decayed teeth, lack of sleep or food, will

[1] *Diagnostic Arithmetic Tests*, F. J. Schonell (Oliver and Boyd). An analysis of these tests is given in Chapter VI.

invariably show weakness in power of sustained attention. His mind will wander so that several figures in a column may be missed, or figures added in twice, or carrying figures left out or put in where they are not necessary. Interest and success improve the way in which the child applies himself. Arithmetic closely related to the pupil's interests and to everyday situations helps to increase intensity of attention during arithmetic lessons.

C. Emotional Causes of Backwardness in Arithmetic

Backwardness in arithmetic is due as much to emotional as to intellectual factors; in fact, after working with backward pupils one is inclined to the conclusion that normal emotional reactions are *more important* than normal intellectual ones to progress in arithmetic. In many cases the confusion, the loss of self-esteem and self-confidence has been so great as almost to inhibit normal intellectual expression; the children have become to all intents and purposes 'number defectives'. Detailed examination of such pupils reveals a number of related emotional troubles—sometimes as many as seven, rarely fewer than three—associated emotional reactions of an adverse type, such as loss of confidence, fear, anxiety, undue fantasy, cheating and compensatory misconduct. Early failure has produced confusion and later difficulties; continued failure has bred a feeling of complete inadequacy in the whole subject. It is clear that these pupils require a measure of individual attention with quick success in arithmetic if they are to be helped.

Apart from the early experiences of some pupils—insufficient early number knowledge, absences, unfortunate teaching methods—that have contributed to their condition, there are often inherent characteristics in the make-up of the child which predispose him to failure in arithmetic. Thus amongst intelligent pupils showing some degree of disability in arithmetic one finds a section of over-emotional, impulsive, over-quick, careless children whose whole life is characterised by very little attention to detail, least of all the finer details of arithmetic, writing and spelling. These pupils have the intellectual power to do their work but are so impulsive that their output is very greatly reduced by inaccuracies. They have often finished their arithmetic first, but their speed is not paralleled by a corresponding level of accuracy. Their work displays all kinds of errors which show little uniformity from day to day. Reporting to the teacher after each sum is completed, and building up a habit of checking, minimise their errors to some extent. Such a procedure should be limited to individuals and never adopted with all the members of the class.

More or less opposite in temperament to the pupils just described are those who exhibit a degree of instability, showing symptoms of nervousness, uncertainty and lack of persistence. A concrete case, taken from a number in my records, aptly illustrates the characteristics of this group. Kathleen D., aged $13\frac{4}{12}$, mental age $12\frac{5}{12}$, had an arithmetic age of only $9\frac{1}{2}$. Her age levels in the different processes and aspects were

Addition	$9\frac{1}{2}$
Subtraction	$10\frac{3}{12}$
Multiplication	10
Division	$10\frac{1}{2}$
Mental	$8\frac{1}{2}$
Rules	$8\frac{1}{2}$
Problems	$7\frac{3}{4}$

The unevenness of her attainments is at once apparent, and these variations are also revealed in the sums she gets right and those she gets wrong. Thus Kathleen fails with

$$\begin{array}{r} 12 \\ 34 \\ 10 \\ 23 \\ \hline 78 \end{array} \qquad \begin{array}{r} 588 \\ 4\overline{)2344} \end{array}$$

but succeeds with

$$\begin{array}{r} 7527{\cdot}4 \\ 3698{\cdot}6 \\ \hline 3828{\cdot}8 \end{array} \qquad \begin{array}{r} 58603 \\ 15\overline{)879045} \end{array}$$

These variations in success and failure were indicative of Kathleen's fluctuating emotional attitudes. Her reactions towards her arithmetic disability varied between apprehension and apathy. Continued failure had produced a dislike of the subject, but the failure was in part due to her inability to apply herself consistently during arithmetic lessons. She was prone to day-dreaming and was particularly interested in drawing, dancing and reading. Her written English was on the whole good. Her meagre arithmetic attainments could be improved through systematic individual assistance, as later remedial work revealed.

Under the heading of emotional causes reference should be made to the atmosphere in which the arithmetic lesson is conducted. Progress in arithmetic is particularly susceptible to the influence of emotional states, and it is a fact well established, both from results of research and from classroom observation, that where a sympathetic, encouraging and stimulating atmosphere is preserved during arithmetic lessons much greater progress is made than where the atmosphere is one of censure, harshness and coercion. Some teachers fail to realise how easily a child may be upset by censure during an arithmetic lesson; it is quite impossible for some children to add, subtract, multiply or divide accurately for some considerable time after they have been upset. Furthermore, many adults make errors in much of the same mechanical work as is set to pupils, yet the child is expected to reach a high standard of accuracy.

Encouraging individual assistance together with a healthy atmosphere of competition and interest are vital nutritives to success in arithmetic.

In concluding this brief survey of causes of backwardness in arithmetic one might stress the importance of the early years in arithmetic teaching, the need for preventing confusion from arising in the mind of the child and the far-reaching psychological effects of failure.

Summary of Causes of Backwardness in Arithmetic

A. Environmental Causes of Backwardness:

(1) Paucity of pre-school experience.
(2) Too early commencement of number with dull pupils.
(3) Other home influences.
(4) Absence from school.
(5) Discontinuity:

(*a*) between infant and junior departments;
(*b*) between school and school or area and area;
(*c*) too rapid promotion;
(*d*) lack of correspondence in syllabuses from school to school.

(6) Teaching methods:

(*a*) over-explanation of processes with duller pupils;
(*b*) over-emphasis of mechanical work;
(*c*) a 'too-extensive' syllabus;
(*d*) commencing a new step before the previous one is mastered;
(*e*) bad grading of examples and an endeavour to teach two similar but not identical types of example in the same lesson.

B. Intellectual Causes of Backwardness:

(1) Deficiency in general intelligence.
(2) Weak memory for numbers.
(3) Weakness in concentration.

C. Emotional Causes of Backwardness:

(1) Psychological effects of failure.
(2) Temperamental disabilities:

(*a*) the impulsive child;
(*b*) the nervous child;
(*c*) the unsympathetic teacher.

CHAPTER V

DIAGNOSIS OF DIFFICULTIES IN ARITHMETIC

As was shown in Chapters I and II the wide variation in arithmetic attainments amongst pupils is due to several factors. Ability to succeed in arithmetic, particularly mental and problem, is dependent upon at least a normal degree of general intelligence, that is on the ability to see relationships and to apply them to new situations. Thus, as there is a wide range in innate intellectual power amongst pupils, it follows that there will be a wide range in arithmetical ability, irrespective of any other conditioning factors.

Furthermore, arithmetic is strikingly susceptible to the influence of emotional attitudes and tendencies. Here again, as there is a wide range in degrees of general emotional stability and in the nature of particular temperamental attitudes amongst pupils, we naturally find that there are pronounced variations in arithmetical attainments if we consider only the emotional equipment of our pupils in relation to their success in arithmetic lessons. Pupils who are nervous, highly strung, unstable or lacking in persistence or concentration show their handicaps soonest and most markedly in arithmetic. A child needs only to be upset for a little or to day-dream for a moment during an arithmetic lesson for his work soon to show the influence of his temporary lapses from stability and concentration. Such lapses may not be important, in say, reading or written composition, but in arithmetic, where final accuracy depends on accuracy in each preceding step, persistent application is necessary on the part of the pupil.

Arithmetic, with its manifold types of sums, each requiring detailed teaching in the initial stages and carefully planned practice in the later ones, is a subject in which the pupil loses undue ground on account of absences, whether they be intermittent or continuous. Owing to a combination of factors, some innate, some environmental, pupils within a school class present to the teacher a great diversity of individual difficulties in arithmetic. Naturally division of the class into sections helps considerably, but even then, with simpler material and with less expected from the more backward pupils, there are still many who flounder because of individual obstacles which have never been satisfactorily surmounted. It is in the full detection of these difficulties that not only the pupil, but also the teacher, requires assistance. A teacher knows the levels of his respective pupils in arithmetic: that John is weak in subtraction, that Lily makes errors in addition and that Ben invariably makes mistakes in multiplication; but what he requires to know exactly is the nature, extent and cause of the pupils' errors in these particular processes. He can then reduce the extent of failure amongst his class by distributing his time and suitable remedial work more effectively.

Nature and Purpose of Diagnostic Tests

If we consider arithmetical attainments from both a qualitative and a quantitative standpoint we can distinguish four main criteria: accuracy, speed of working, methods of work and extent of arithmetical processes mastered. Obviously some of these essentials are relatively more important than others; their values differ with pupils of different ages and different mental calibres. For our normally intelligent pupils who will pass to some form of selective post-primary education all four criteria are important; with duller pupils accuracy is the outstanding necessity, but speed, methods of working and range of processes known also need consideration. It is obvious that a class teacher obtains through the medium of his classwork and through weekly or monthly tests an indication of his pupils' ability in each of the four directions. But this is not enough for teaching purposes, particularly with those pupils who are backward in their work; with them he requires a more analytic estimate of their achievements. In this he can obtain help from two sources:

(*a*) the use of diagnostic tests;

(*b*) a knowledge of common errors in the fundamental processes.

By these two aids he can *achieve the purpose*, not only of diagnosing difficulties, but of apportioning suitable remedial material on scientific lines and of preventing further errors.

(*a*) *Diagnostic Tests*

A diagnostic test in any school subject is constructed for the specific purpose of analysing the exact nature of the progress made by pupils in each important aspect of the subject. The test takes into consideration all the vital skills involved in each important aspect and these are tested by a series of carefully graded examples which cover all important steps in the acquirement of the skill. Thus a diagnostic test differs from an ordinary classroom test and from a standardised scholastic test in so far as its main object is to analyse, not to assess. It differs too in neglecting the speed factor, for in a diagnostic test ample time is provided for pupils to complete all they are able to do. Differences between diagnostic and the usual standardised attainment tests are made clear if we consider examples of tests in a particular aspect of a particular subject.

Thus in arithmetic, in one standardised subtraction test[1] the pupils are given 5 minutes in which to work as many as possible of this type of subtraction exercise:

9802	7721	4944	3208	5381
6246	1841	1295	1738	3676

The emphasis in this instance is on speed and accuracy in an advanced form of subtraction, and the level attained by the pupil can be estimated from a table of averages devised from application of the test to large numbers of pupils of different ages. Some estimate of a pupil's ability in subtraction may

[1] C. Burt, *Mental and Scholastic Tests*, (P. S. King and Son), pp. 300, 302 and 367

also be obtained from a standardised mechanical arithmetic test by examining the pupil's results in those items involving subtraction. Thus in *The Essential Mechanical Arithmetic Test*, Form A,[1] a teacher may gain some information of the testee's facility in subtraction from items 4, 5, 6, 14, 19, 23 and 28.

A further form of subtraction test,[2] which is particularly applicable to young, and to dull and backward children, is that compiled and standardised by Sleight. In this, more attention has been paid to grading, and the test consists of forty examples ranging in difficulty from 5—2 to 7572—3724. A time limit of 3 minutes is set.

Although all these tests enable a general estimate of speed and accuracy in subtraction to be made by means of the carefully compiled averages for pupils of different ages, yet none of them is fully diagnostic in the sense that it presents all possible steps in subtraction, arranged in order of difficulty, so that the exact level of the pupil's mastery of subtraction and the exact location of his weaknesses can be discovered. It is just this objective that characterises the diagnostic test; it aims at gathering information on all aspects of the subtraction process, irrespective of the speed factor, at finding out just what the pupil can do and the precise step at which his knowledge breaks down.

Hence in a diagnostic test in subtraction the first sub-test consists of the 100 basic combinations of numbers under 20, which are essential to all subtraction exercises, for example:

9—2	9—4	10—5	7—0	8—5
11—2	10—6	12—8	14—7	12—9
8—3	10—8	11—5	10—9	11—8

The pupils work all combinations and from the results the teacher can tell what degree of mastery of these fundamental facts has been attained by each pupil. He learns what are the

[1] *The Essential Mechanical Arithmetic Test*, Forms A and B, compiled by F. J. Schonell (Oliver and Boyd). These are 30-minute standardised tests which include examples in the four rules, together with applications to money and to common weights and measures.

[2] G. F. Sleight, *Diagnosis and Treatment of the Dull and Backward Child* (Ph.D. thesis, University of London), p. 272

individual failings and whether they are numerous or isolated; and he learns what, if any, are the failings of the class as a whole. With this information before him he can determine whether or not the pupils can reasonably be expected to succeed with more difficult examples.

The next sub-test is based on an adequate sampling of all the vital steps in subtraction in their order of difficulty. Four examples are allotted to each step. The first step is quite simple subtraction in which there is no 'borrowing',[1] and there are only tens and units in the minuend and units in the subtrahend, thus:

$$\begin{array}{r} 98 \\ -\ 3 \\ \hline \\ \hline \end{array} \qquad \begin{array}{r} 57 \\ -\ 4 \\ \hline \\ \hline \end{array}$$

In the next step there are tens and units in both minuend and subtrahend, but no 'borrowing', thus:

$$\begin{array}{r} 55 \\ -32 \\ \hline \\ \hline \end{array} \qquad \begin{array}{r} 99 \\ -43 \\ \hline \\ \hline \end{array}$$

while the third step extends this form of subtraction, *i.e.* without 'borrowing', to three figures in both minuend and subtrahend, thus:

$$\begin{array}{r} 346 \\ -215 \\ \hline \\ \hline \end{array} \qquad \begin{array}{r} 987 \\ -832 \\ \hline \\ \hline \end{array}$$

Step four involves this form of example:

$$\begin{array}{r} 18 \\ -14 \\ \hline \\ \hline \end{array} \qquad \begin{array}{r} 16 \\ -10 \\ \hline \\ \hline \end{array}$$

i.e. a simple introduction to '0' difficulties.

[1] The term 'borrowing' is used throughout the book in inverted commas. It is not meant to refer only to the decomposition method of subtraction but also to the equal addition method, and hence is used as a convenient term covering the step of adding ten to the minuend and adding a compensating ten to the subtrahend.

The next step introduces the pupil to simple 'borrowing', but with, in the subtrahend, a unit figure only thus:

$$\begin{array}{r} 71 \\ -\ 2 \\ \hline \\ \hline \end{array} \qquad \begin{array}{r} 62 \\ -\ 4 \\ \hline \\ \hline \end{array}$$

This is then extended by a very small increase in difficulty to the form in which there is 'borrowing' only in the units column, but there are two figures in both minuend and subtrahend; for example:

$$\begin{array}{r} 54 \\ -39 \\ \hline \\ \hline \end{array} \qquad \begin{array}{r} 22 \\ -17 \\ \hline \\ \hline \end{array}$$

In this manner the diagnostic subtraction test proceeds by a further eight steps, each involving a slight increase in difficulty until the final example:

$$\begin{array}{r} 6067 \\ -5970 \\ \hline \\ \hline \end{array}$$

represents a high-water mark in subtraction ability.

In preceding paragraphs we have examined two diagnostic sub-tests in subtraction, but naturally a complete battery of such tests would include a similar consideration of other processes, addition, multiplication and division. A further extension would include graded material in fractions, decimals and percentages. It is quite clear from our detailed consideration of the diagnostic tests in subtraction that the teacher will obtain from the use of such tests much valuable information of an exceedingly systematised and individualised kind. The results will reveal, at one testing and in a comprehensive way, the *exact* level reached by his pupils and the *precise* nature of their difficulties. There will be no hit or miss about the examination and nothing will be left to chance; the teacher will realise that instead of having to discover at random the subtraction difficulties of his pupils through their everyday work—a very unsatisfactory method—he has in the results of the diagnostic test a complete inventory of their subtraction attainments.

Similarly the diagnostic tests in the other processes will discover for him the pupils' exact equipment in addition, multiplication and division. And it must be borne in mind that automatic accuracy in the basic combinations and in the simpler forms of the fundamental processes is the foundation of all arithmetic.

(*b*) *Knowledge of Common Errors in the Four Rules*

By far the most valuable approach to the diagnosis of difficulties in arithmetic is made by using a carefully constructed diagnostic test, but results from these can be made even more useful if they are supplemented by information on the pupils' methods of working and on the reasons for their errors. In many cases this information can be derived from a scrutiny of the pupils' work, but there are some instances, particularly with pupils who are very backward in arithmetic, where it is necessary to make observation of their arithmetical habits and to employ oral analysis of their written work.

The most useful way of obtaining an insight into a pupil's arithmetical methods is to ask him to work aloud a number of significant examples from the diagnostic tests, including steps where he has made errors. Methods of working, especially in addition, but also in all sums where more difficult number combinations are involved, should be noted. Here a word of warning is necessary. The atmosphere in the classroom during arithmetic is of vital importance and the teacher must see that this oral analysis does not become oral inquisition. There are some teachers who do too much working aloud of sums with their backward pupils. This is bad, not only because it deprives such pupils of the very independence and initiative in arithmetic which the teachers are seeking to develop, but also because some children, frequently nervous ones and those labouring under inferiority attitudes, make more mistakes when all their working is done aloud than when it is done silently.[1] At the same time oral analysis in doubtful cases is helpful, and in this respect examination of the pupil's methods is made simpler and more effective if we are conversant with the common errors in the four processes. For example, if we know that in column addition, as well as the obvious mistakes such as errors in combinations (39+7=45), failure to carry, or omission of a number, there are other less obvious mistakes such as adding in the carrying number irregularly—sometimes first, sometimes last, sometimes in the middle of the column—or useless splitting of numbers, *e.g.* 49+6=49+1=50+5=55, then we have prior knowledge that makes our oral examination of the child's work both keener and more effective. Hence schedules of common errors in the four rules, in order of importance, together with examples of these, are a further means by which the diagnosis of pupils' difficulties can be made with both speed and accuracy.

We now turn to a more detailed discussion of specific diagnostic tests in arithmetic, namely the *Schonell Diagnostic Arithmetic Tests*,[2] and to the examination of schedules of common errors compiled from experience with them.

[1] The fact is not neglected that there are also a few pupils of the reverse type who work sums orally but are inaccurate in written arithmetic.

[2] These are published in a sixteen-page booklet and also in *Diagnostic and Attainment Testing* by F. J. and F. E. Schonell (Oliver and Boyd). It will be found helpful if a copy of the test is used for reference in conjunction with the reading of Chapter VI.

These diagnostic tests in the four rules have been supplemented by similar tests for discovering pupils' difficulties in fractions, decimals and percentages. See *Diagnostic Tests in Fractions, Decimals and Percentages* by F. J. Schonell, J. Richardson and K. P. O'Connor (Oliver and Boyd, 1956).

CHAPTER VI

THE SCHONELL DIAGNOSTIC ARITHMETIC TESTS: THEIR NATURE AND ADMINISTRATION

THE *Schonell Diagnostic Arithmetic Tests* consist of twelve tests constructed for the purpose of gauging levels of attainment and for locating individual difficulties in addition, subtraction, multiplication, division (short and long) and simple mental problems. The tests are as follows:

Test 1. Addition (100 basic number combinations).
Test 2. Subtraction (100 basic number combinations).
Test 3. Multiplication (100 basic number combinations).
Test 4. Division (90 basic number combinations).
Test 5. Miscellaneous (difficult number combinations in the four processes together with the more difficult examples in multiplication and division by 10, 11, 12).
Test 6. Graded Addition.
Test 7. Graded Subtraction.
Test 8A and B. Graded Multiplication.
Test 9. Graded Division.
Test 10. Graded Long Division (easy steps).
Test 11. Graded Long Division (harder steps).
Test 12. Graded Mental Arithmetic.

NATURE OF EACH TEST

In the following pages the nature of each test is dealt with in detail—content, construction and values being considered.

Test 1. *Addition*

This test consists of the 100 basic addition facts which cover all combinations of numbers under 10, inclusive of zero combinations. There is an approximate progression of difficulty throughout the series, but no serious attempt has been made in this direction, for modern research shows that degree of difficulty in the various number combinations in the four processes differs considerably from pupil to pupil. A combination that is easy for one pupil to master is difficult for another and *vice versa*—a point which indicates the paramount importance of tracing the difficulties of each individual. Combinations are also given in two forms, for it is found that not infrequently a pupil who knows 9+7=16 may fail with 7+9. The material is arranged in groups of five combinations across the page and in twenty columns down the page, with letters across and down to indicate exact positions of lines and items when the test is being given or corrected orally. The first and last three lines of the test are reproduced below:

TEST 1. ADDITION

These are all ADD sums.

Work across the page.

	(*a*)	(*b*)	(*c*)	(*d*)	(*e*)
A	1+1=	0+0=	2+2=	2+1=	1+3=
B	2+0=	3+1=	3+3=	5+5=	4+1=
C	1+6=	4+0=	4+4=	1+7=	6+1=
R	7+5=	5+9=	4+9=	8+6=	7+8=
S	9+5=	8+7=	6+9=	9+8=	9+7=
T	6+8=	9+6=	8+5=	5+8=	7+9=

The value of the test lies in the fact that, in so far as it includes all basic combinations, it is a means of systematically assessing the pupil's attainments in simple addition. It shows whether any particular combination, through accident or wrong association, has remained unknown or uncertain. To some extent the teacher would discover, during ordinary arithmetic lessons, a number of the deficiencies that the test reveals in his pupils, but it is also clear from experience that large numbers of individual errors remain undetected. For example, use of the test with a girl aged 11, very backward in arithmetic, showed that, amongst other errors, she always made the mistake 9+6=14 and had been consistently inaccurate in this combination for months past.

Naturally the test is not free from the possibility of chance inaccuracy, *i.e.*, from slips, through speed or slackening of concentration, that pupils normally make, but these are few. Where a combination is wrong in one form only, the inaccuracy may be due to chance or to limited knowledge, but where it is wrong in both forms (*e.g.* 6+7=11, 7+6=11) the teacher can be fairly certain that the combination is not known by the child. Furthermore, as with tests of basic combinations in the other processes, so in addition, one can verify the nature of the error by testing the combination again orally. A major value of the test is that it determines how far pupils, particularly younger and more backward ones, have proceeded with abstract addition. If the number of errors in the test is very great it is quite clear that the pupil is not ready to proceed with addition 'sums'; he has not successfully bridged that gulf from the concrete to the abstract, and it is a waste of the teacher's time to require him to add 26 and 83 when he has not mastered the basic combinations involved. He requires to be turned back to simpler material with concrete aids, or alternatively he should use concrete counting aids while doing his simple addition sums.[1]

Higher Decade Addition

A final point of importance is that concerning higher decade addition. The discerning teacher may observe that a child knows 2+7, but does not correctly add 52+7, or gives the correct answer to 6+9, but errs in 36+9, and he will be led to ask, 'How far is there transfer from the simple combinations to the higher decade combinations?' In other words, if pupils know all the 100 basic combinations under 10, are they likely to succeed with the same combinations in numbers over 10? The answer is that most pupils of normal or supernormal intelligence make the necessary transfer, but dull pupils and those experiencing difficulty with arithmetic require further aid.

Similarly, there is a certain amount of addition in multiplication sums, for the higher decade addition combinations

[1] Details of remedial teaching are given in Chapter VIII.

involved in multiplication will always have as their basis a multiplication fact, *e.g.*

$$\begin{array}{r} 429 \\ \times 9 \\ \hline \\ \hline \end{array}$$

Here the pupil multiplies 9 by 9 (81), puts down 1 and carries 8, 9×2 (18), 18 and 8 are 26, puts down 6 and carries 2, 9×4 (36), 36 and 2 are 38.

Teachers may require to know to what extent pupils can transfer their basic knowledge, so to cover the requirements for higher decade addition in both addition and multiplication I have prepared, in book form,[1] graded material covering 240 of the higher decade addition facts requiring bridging and 168 of the higher decade addition facts used in multiplication.[2]

Test 2. *Subtraction*

This test, similar in pattern to Test 1, consists of the 100 basic subtraction combinations which are fundamental, not only to subtraction itself, but also to division and to simple problems. The test enables the teacher to examine scientifically all his pupils in all subtraction combinations, not once but a number of times, and then to distribute drill according to individual needs.

The first and last three lines of the test are as follows:

TEST 2. SUBTRACTION

These are all SUBTRACT or TAKE AWAY sums.

Work across the page.

	(*a*)	(*b*)	(*c*)	(*d*)	(*e*)
A	3−2=	1−1=	4−2=	5−4=	0−0=
B	5−3=	3−3=	5−1=	4−4=	8−1=
C	6−6=	4−3=	3−1=	2−1=	6−5=
R	14−8=	15−9=	13−8=	15−6=	13−5=
S	14−6=	13−4=	17−8=	16−9=	13−7=
T	17−9=	14−5=	14−9=	13−9=	16−7=

[1] *Practice in Basic Arithmetic*, Book Two, by F. J. Schonell (Oliver and Boyd, 1954). See also *Teacher's Handbook to 'Practice in Basic Arithmetic'* for information on higher decade addition.

[2] The use of these for remedial work is discussed in Chapter VIII. 'Bridging' means breaking into the next ten.

The combinations have been arranged in approximate order of difficulty, but here as in other processes there is considerable variation from pupil to pupil in the difficulty presented by any one pair of units.

With dull pupils and those backward in arithmetic it is useful to notice the errors in subtraction compared with those in addition and to see how far the pupil views them as two entirely different processes and how far he sees some relationship between them. There are some pupils, backward in arithmetic, who have never been shown the relationship between such combinations as $15-8=7$, $8+7=15$, and $15-7=8$.

The combinations most frequently incorrect are: $11-6$, $16-9$, $17-9$, $15-6$, $13-4$, $14-6$, $13-8$, $11-3$.

More errors in calculation and more substitution of another process occur in this test than in addition. Basic subtraction combinations, as with addition, also have their higher decade forms (*e.g.* $59-54$, $68-63$), many of which appear in division sums. And teachers may wish to discover the pupil's ability with the applied forms of subtraction. Hence, for diagnostic and for practice purposes, I have prepared material covering all the important higher decade subtraction facts required in division.[1]

Test 3. *Multiplication*

This test provides a measure of the pupil's attainments in his multiplication tables up to 9 times. But the material is not set out in the conventional form of $1\times2=2$, $2\times2=4$, $3\times2=6$ etc., for there are many pupils who have so mechanically memorised the multiplication facts that when they require a certain item, say 6×8, they have to run through in their minds all the preceding facts in the table before they can give a response. On the contrary the test contains the multiplication combinations set out in jumbled form. To facilitate testing in multiplication of 7-year-old pupils in infant classes, where the aim is to teach up to the 6 times table, all combinations up to 9×6 have been grouped in the first 11 lines (A-K) of the test. A line

[1] See pp. 8-10 of *Practice in Basic Arithmetic*, Book Two, by F. J. Schonell (Oliver and Boyd, 1954).

separates these from the remainder of the test, but naturally most pupils would do the entire series. Combinations have been used in two forms, *e.g.* 6×7= and 7×6= , while all possible '0' difficulties, *e.g.* 0×0, and 9×0 and 0×7, have been included.

The first and last three lines of the test are reproduced below:

TEST 3. MULTIPLICATION

These are all MULTIPLY or TIMES sums.

Work across the page.

	(*a*)	(*b*)	(*c*)	(*d*)	(*e*)
A	1×3=	2×2=	1×7=	2×1=	1×4=
B	5×1=	2×5=	1×6=	2×8=	1×5=
C	4×1=	2×3=	1×8=	3×2=	2×9=
R	8×7=	7×9=	3×0=	9×6=	7×7=
S	8×0=	6×0=	7×8=	8×5=	0×2=
T	9×7=	9×3=	0×1=	0×7=	9×4=

Use of the test reveals the elements in the multiplication tables that have been insufficiently memorised. It also emphasises the need to teach all combinations in both forms; the pupil who gets 4×9 right but 9×4 wrong has not only learnt these as unrelated items but has, in all probability, given insufficient attention to 9×4 because it was considered that 4×9 in the 4 times table would transfer to the item in reverse form in the 9 times table. Such an assumption is, in the main, not justified by the results of this test.

The most difficult combinations are: 9×6, 7×8, 9×7 and all the zero combinations.

Test 4. *Division*

Test 4 provides a comprehensive survey of the 90 basic division facts. As in Test 3 they are arranged so that lines A-K include division by numbers from 1 to 6, while lines L-S cover division by 7, 8 and 9 and the '0' difficulties. This arrangement facilitates the testing of pupils in upper classes of infant departments.

The first and last three lines of the test are as follows:

TEST 4. DIVISION

These are all DIVIDE sums.
Work across the page.

	(*a*)	(*b*)	(*c*)	(*d*)	(*e*)
A	4÷2=	10÷2=	9÷3=	6÷2=	10÷5=
B	15÷3=	8÷2=	14÷2=	20÷5=	25÷5=
C	12÷2=	16÷2=	12÷6=	12÷3=	15÷5=
P	0÷2=	42÷7=	0÷5=	36÷9=	0÷7=
Q	48÷8=	63÷7=	0÷8=	64÷8=	63÷9=
R	0÷9=	54÷9=	7÷7=	56÷8=	9÷9=

As with the multiplication combinations, so in division, facts involving 0s cause the greatest number of errors, while 54÷9, 54÷6, 42÷7, 24÷3, 2÷2, 3÷3, 4÷4, 5÷5, 6÷6, 7÷7, 8÷8, 9÷9 also occasion difficulty.

The 90 combinations which form Test 4 are fundamental to all arithmetic progress and should be rendered automatic by all pupils. These division facts are, however, without remainders so that there still exist 535 simple division facts that have remainders. Now although children may transfer much of their knowledge of the basic division facts to these, there is the need to provide practice in those division facts with remainders in which children make most errors. Accordingly such material for diagnostic or for practice purposes—comprising 336 important division facts with remainders graded in order of difficulty—has been included in Book Two of *Practice in Basic Arithmetic*.

COMPARISON OF RESULTS IN TESTS 1 TO 4

As well as revealing individual errors in the basic combinations in the four processes, Tests 1 to 4 provide evidence on the relative degrees to which pupils have mastered the fundamental facts in addition, subtraction, multiplication and division. This important information is soon shown by a tabulation of results.

For example, amongst the tabulated scores of 93 9-year-old pupils in a junior school the following variations in accuracy were to be noted:

Pupils	Possible Scores			
	Addn. 100	Subn. 100	Multn. 100	Divn. 90
E. B.	97	98	97	74
J. P.	99	92	88	86
L. B.	99	99	90	52
R. S.	100	88	82	86
M. P.	97	99	96	67
R. V.	96	83	96	71
S. L.	100	90	85	84
F. P.	100	78	73	90

It is obvious that different pupils require practice in different fundamentals to bring them up to a normal level of efficiency. Thus we note that L.B., although up to average in three processes, is particularly weak in division, whereas F.P. makes maximum scores in addition and division but shows definite weakness in subtraction and multiplication.

Not only does such a comparison show deficiencies in particular processes, but it also throws into relief the general weakness of some pupils. For example, in the group mentioned above there were:

J. L.	95	67	65	38
D. W.	94	71	70	62

Yet these pupils were endeavouring to work sums involving hundreds, carrying and 'borrowing'.

It cannot be too strongly urged that every teacher should consider, in tabulated form, the results of all his pupils in Tests 1 to 4. Time thus spent will be amply repaid in later work in arithmetic.

Test 5. *Miscellaneous*

The first fourteen lines of this test consist of seventy of the most difficult combinations in the four processes, as contained in Tests 1 to 4. The combinations are arranged in mixed order and are primarily for discovering the pupil's efficiency in changing from one process to another.

Examination of errors in arithmetic shows that certain pupils are unable to keep before them the single idea necessary for continuing with the same kind of response when dealing with groups of figures. Thus, instead of continuing to add in a particular set of exercises, they will change to multiplication or subtraction. Usually the direction of their ideas is changed by a combination of figures which has a stronger appeal in some process other than the one being used. In reverse manner some pupils experience difficulty in changing from one process to another. For example, after two additions they will continue to add where a multiplication sign indicates a change of operation. Test 5 shows the degree of facility pupils possess in responding to the more difficult combinations in the four rules when the process changes frequently.

The last thirty elements in the test consist of a selection of the most difficult combinations from the multiplication and division tables of 10, 11 and 12.

The first and last three lines of the test are shown below:

TEST 5. MISCELLANEOUS

There are FOUR kinds of sums here, ADD, SUBTRACT, MULTIPLY, DIVIDE.

Work across the page.

	(*a*)	(*b*)	(*c*)	(*d*)	(*e*)
A	3+ 8=	12− 5=	7× 6=	3+ 9=	42÷ 7=
B	27÷ 3=	5× 0=	12− 7=	11− 4=	15− 7=
C	9+ 3=	36÷ 9=	7× 9=	7+ 6=	8+ 9=
R	72÷12=	11×10=	11× 8=	132÷12=	12×11=
S	11× 9=	77÷11=	144÷12=	12×12=	110÷11=
T	48÷12=	12× 5=	99÷11=	132÷11=	12× 9=

It is sometimes useful, particularly with older pupils, to discover their levels in speed and accuracy with the basic materials provided in Tests 1 to 5. Therefore in Appendix I on pages 181-85 we have set out the average scores and equivalent arithmetic ages (based on 2,400 pupils between the ages of 7·0 and 14·11) when time limits are set.

Test 1	3 minutes
Test 2	3½ minutes
Test 3	3 minutes
Test 4	3 minutes
Test 5	5 minutes

All pupils actually wrote their answers on the test paper. It is apparent, therefore, that if a pupil's scores are to be compared with the average scores given, the test must be conducted under similar conditions, that is, Tests 1 to 5 cannot be taken orally, nor can the answers be written on a previously prepared answer sheet. The answer must be written in the test booklet if a comparative estimate of combined speed and accuracy is required.

This use of the test booklet does not preclude a full diagnostic value being obtained; for, after the tests have been marked, the teacher can still allow pupils to complete each of the tests in their own time and thus discover any individual difficulties.

Test 6. *Graded Addition*

In Test 6 a complete inventory of all reasonable steps in ordinary addition has been provided. The steps have been graded in order of difficulty and four examples of the same type have been allotted to each step. Preliminary trials with this type of diagnostic test show that four examples are sufficient to provide reliable evidence regarding the pupil's degree of mastery of succeeding phases in the four rules. If a pupil fails in all examples of a particular step or gets only one correct, then it can be safely assumed that he is unfamiliar with the actual nature of the step. Of course, it might be that he is grossly inaccurate in the basic combinations involved in the step, but if this is a general condition, which can be determined from the results of Tests 1 to 5, then it amounts to the same thing as not knowing the step, for it means that the pupil's basic knowledge in addition, subtraction, multiplication or division is so uncertain that he requires considerably more experience with the concrete and with drills before being allowed to try the more difficult phases of a process. If, on the other hand, a pupil succeeds with three or four of the examples allotted to a step, it is safe to assume that he is at least conversant with the aspect of the process that the step represents.

In the test booklet there are eight examples to a line, *i.e.* two testing units; for example, the first two lines are as follows:

TEST 6. GRADED ADDITION

These are all ADD sums.

Work across the page.

	(*a*)	(*b*)	(*c*)	(*d*)	(*e*)	(*f*)	(*g*)	(*h*)
A	14 3	15 4	12 6	2 17	10 15	13 16	12 14	11 10
	—	—	—	—	—	—	—	—
	—	—	—	—	—	—	—	—
	(*a*)	(*b*)	(*c*)	(*d*)	(*e*)	(*f*)	(*g*)	(*h*)
B	31 66	65 22	23 73	28 30	123 45	346 212	482 305	543 126
	—	—	—	—	—	—	—	—
	—	—	—	—	—	—	—	—

These examples represent four steps in the addition test. Below, each unit of four examples is set out separately, with a description of the step it is designed to test. This arrangement will facilitate the later interpretation of results and the distribution of remedial work.

1st step

14 3	15 4	12 6	2 17	Tens (under 20) in one line, units in the other; no carrying.
—	—	—	—	
—	—	—	—	

2nd step

10 15	13 16	12 14	11 10	Tens (under 20) in both lines; 0's introduced; no carrying.
—	—	—	—	
—	—	—	—	

3rd step

31	65	23	28	Tens (over 20) in both lines; no carrying.
66	22	73	30	

4th step

123	346	482	543	Hundreds and tens in both lines; no carrying.
45	212	305	126	

5th step

9	15	6	9	Units in one line, tens (under 20) in the other; carrying.
19	6	17	17	

6th step

57	58	6	8	Units in one line, tens (over 20) in the other; carrying.
7	6	89	68	

7th step

87	96	84	50	Tens in both lines, carrying in tens place.
31	63	94	81	

8th step

23	39	14	37	Tens in both lines, carrying in units place.
17	48	79	59	

9th step

401	209	874	635	Numbers over 100 in one or both lines; carrying in units, tens or hundreds place.
607	39	83	944	

10th step

56	38	57	54	Tens in both lines; carrying in both units and tens places.
69	86	59	97	

11th step

74	38	46	86	Column addition, 3 lines; numbers under 100; carrying.
56	78	37	48	
43	94	96	39	

12th step

897	953	765	925	Hundreds, tens and units in both lines; carrying in 2 or 3 places.
497	818	488	469	

13th step

77	94			Column addition, 4 lines of 2 figures; 3 lines of 3 figures.
48	83	277	126	
32	76	183	848	
65	59	149	976	

14th step

28	608	3	951	Variations in column addition introducing difficult number combinations.
103	705	81	382	
784	33	19	467	
9	219	827	539	
		94	196	

At the conclusion of the test there are two examples of addition in a horizontal setting:

$6+4+9+7+8+5+3+9=$

$9+8+7+6+5+8+7+3+2+0+7=$

With the aid of the above analysis the teacher can examine the results achieved by his pupils, particularly the backward ones, and find the exact level that they have reached in addition. The field of possible error is covered step by step so that with all pupils, irrespective of age or arithmetical attainments, the teacher is enabled to detect weak spots in this process. This systematic review of all possible difficulties not only provides the teacher with the necessary information for future class work in the addition process but also makes it possible for him to give the exact aid required by individual pupils.[1]

All types of errors are exposed by the test. For example, it was clear from the test that Ruth S., aged $8\frac{9}{12}$, had never learnt to carry. She worked the first sixteen sums correctly but after that all her efforts were of this type:

$$\begin{array}{r} 9 \\ 19 \\ \hline 118 \end{array} \quad \begin{array}{r} 15 \\ 6 \\ \hline 111 \end{array} \quad \begin{array}{r} 6 \\ 17 \\ \hline 113 \end{array} \quad \begin{array}{r} 9 \\ 17 \\ \hline 116 \end{array}$$

$$\begin{array}{r} 57 \\ 7 \\ \hline 514 \end{array} \quad \begin{array}{r} 58 \\ 6 \\ \hline 514 \end{array} \quad \begin{array}{r} 6 \\ 89 \\ \hline 815 \end{array} \quad \begin{array}{r} 7 \\ 68 \\ \hline 615 \end{array}$$

In other cases the results show evidence of persistent errors in certain combinations; thus Eileen B., aged $9\frac{5}{12}$, makes these mistakes:

$$\begin{array}{r} 96 \\ 63 \\ \hline 129 \end{array} \quad \begin{array}{r} 635 \\ 944 \\ \hline 1279 \end{array} \quad \begin{array}{r} 56 \\ 69 \\ \hline 122 \end{array}$$

For this pupil $9+6=12$.

Types of carrying errors are also plainly revealed; whereas some pupils will correctly carry figures over 1 they frequently make a mistake when the carrying figure is 1. These and other types of error are discussed, from the point of view of frequency and importance, in a later section.

[1] Remedial material on each of these steps is provided in *Practice in Basic Arithmetic*, Book Three, pp. 1-4.

Test 7. Graded Subtraction

The principle of this test is similar to that of Test 6. The aim is to cover by successive steps of increasing difficulty all the major steps in the process of subtraction. Four examples are selected to test each step, and two of these units of four, that is eight examples, appear in each of the seven lines of the test booklet. To explain the test fully and to assist the teacher in the examination of results, each step is here considered separately:

1st step

98	57	84	38	Tens and units in minuend; units in
3	4	1	8	subtrahend; no borrowing.

2nd step

55	99	78	97	Tens and units in minuend and
32	43	10	22	subtrahend; no borrowing.

3rd step

346	987	378	496	Hundreds, tens and units in minuend
215	832	122	261	and subtrahend; no borrowing.

4th step

18	19	16	17	Numbers less than 20. Unit digit
14	18	10	15	in subtrahend less than unit digit in
				minuend; tens digits both unity.

5th step

71	62	46	84	Tens in minuend; units in subtra-
2	4	7	6	hend; borrowing.

6th step

54	22	58	46	Tens and units in minuend and subtrahend; borrowing in units.
39	17	19	27	

7th step

331	543	283	786	Hundreds, tens and units in minuend; borrowing in units.
18	25	29	58	

8th step

316	564	68	387	Borrowing in units and tens or borrowing in units and zero result in tens.
27	59	59	299	

9th step

980	168	80	430	Introduction of zero difficulty in units or tens.
930	68	57	416	

10th step

180	250	160	890	Examples of $\genfrac{}{}{0pt}{}{0}{1}$ and $\genfrac{}{}{0pt}{}{0}{9}$ difficulties.
71	49	31	889	

11th step

346	629	756	387	Borrowing in tens place. Numbers over 100.
284	473	382	196	

12th step

364	831	8354	8112	Borrowing in hundreds, tens and units places.
295	276	5676	6798	

13th step

800	607	700	906	Advanced '0' difficulties and borrowing.
695	298	192	199	

14th step

891	904	705	6067	Advanced '0' difficulties and borrowing.
207	206	109	5970	

The above examination of the test makes it apparent that any difficulty in subtraction would be revealed by use of the test.

Particularly does the test show the nature of carrying errors prevalent amongst children, and the widespread difficulties occasioned by like numbers and by noughts in subtraction. These latter points are clearly portrayed in the results achieved by Kenneth R., aged 10:

1st step. One error

38
8
38

2nd and 3rd steps. No errors.

4th step. Four errors.

18	19	16	17
14	18	10	15
14	11	16	12

5th, 6th, 7th and 8th steps. No errors.

9th step. Two errors.

80	430
57	416
30	426

10th step. Four errors.

180	250	160	890
71	49	31	889
111	219	131	819

11th and 12th steps. No errors.

6th step

54 39	22 17	58 19	46 27	Tens and units in minuend and subtrahend; borrowing in units.

7th step

331 18	543 25	283 29	786 58	Hundreds, tens and units in minuend; borrowing in units.

8th step

316 27	564 59	68 59	387 299	Borrowing in units and tens or borrowing in units and zero result in tens.

9th step

980 930	168 68	80 57	430 416	Introduction of zero difficulty in units or tens.

10th step

180 71	250 49	160 31	890 889	Examples of $\begin{array}{c}0\\1\end{array}$ and $\begin{array}{c}0\\9\end{array}$ difficulties.

11th step

346 284	629 473	756 382	387 196	Borrowing in tens place. Numbers over 100.

12th step

364 295	831 276	8354 5676	8112 6798	Borrowing in hundreds, tens and units places.

13th step

800	607	700	906	Advanced '0' difficulties and borrowing.
695	298	192	199	

14th step

891	904	705	6067	Advanced '0' difficulties and borrowing.
207	206	109	5970	

The above examination of the test makes it apparent that any difficulty in subtraction would be revealed by use of the test.

Particularly does the test show the nature of carrying errors prevalent amongst children, and the widespread difficulties occasioned by like numbers and by noughts in subtraction. These latter points are clearly portrayed in the results achieved by Kenneth R., aged 10:

1st step. One error

38
8
38

2nd and 3rd steps. No errors.

4th step. Four errors.

18	19	16	17
14	18	10	15
14	11	16	12

5th, 6th, 7th and 8th steps. No errors.

9th step. Two errors.

80	430
57	416
30	426

10th step. Four errors.

180	250	160	890
71	49	31	889
111	219	131	819

11th and 12th steps. No errors.

13th step. Four errors.

800	607	700	906
695	298	192	199
295	509	692	907

14th step. Three errors.

904	705	6067
206	109	5970
708	616	1917

The nature of Kenneth's errors with like numbers and with noughts, both in consistency and in extent, is amply illustrated.[1]

The individual form of difficulties in arithmetic and the illogicality of their causal basis are clearly revealed only by the use of diagnostic tests; thus Kenneth can correctly work the apparently difficult examples in the 12th step:

8354	and	8112
5676		6798

because they do not contain like figures or '0' difficulties, but he fails with simple sums like

18	160	180
14	31	71

Test 8A and B. Graded Multiplication

This test provides a gauge of attainment in multiplication, simple and compound. From a very simple example (22×4) the test proceeds by steps of increasing difficulty to exercises in three figure multiplication (7080×605). As in Tests 6 and 7 there are four items of similar type to each step, but in order to allow adequate space for working items in the test booklet, only six examples are allotted to each line on the first page of the test and three on the second page. Thus on the first page

[1] Remedial or practice material consisting of graded examples on each step in the diagnostic subtraction test is provided on pp. 5-10 of Book Three of *Practice in Basic Arithmetic*.

of the test a line contains four examples of one step and two of the succeeding step, which is completed on the next line with two more examples. The first two lines of the test, containing twelve examples, *i.e.* three steps, are as follows:

	(*a*)	(*b*)	(*c*)	(*d*)	(*e*)	(*f*)
A	22 4	31 5	63 2	91 5	423 3	612 4
B	711 5	843 2	60 6	303 3	400 8	9010 5

There are in the complete test fourteen steps embracing fifty-three examples.[1] These, with descriptive details, are set out below:

1st step

22 4	31 5	63 2	91 5	Simple multiplication, 2 figures in multiplicand; no carrying.

2nd step

423 3	612 4	711 5	843 2	Simple multiplication, 3 figures in multiplicand; no carrying.

3rd step

60 6	303 3	400 8	9010 5	Simple multiplication, 2, 3 or 4 figures in multiplicand. '0' difficulties introduced; no carrying.

4th step

18 9	17 5	16 7	19 7	Simple multiplication; carrying into tens place.

[1] Remedial material for remedial teaching or for practice in each step in the test is provided on pp. 11-18 of Book Three of *Practice in Basic Arithmetic*.

5th step

76 9 — —	86 8 — —	96 6 — —	87 4 — —	Simple multiplication, multiplicand over 20; carrying into tens place.

6th step

104 9 — —	106 7 — —	8050 11 — —	7004 8 — —	Simple multiplication, numbers over 100. '0' difficulties; carrying.

7th step

348 12 — —	4196 11 — —	95347 12 — —	874615 9 — —	Simple multiplication, 3 to 6 figures in multiplicand; carrying.

8th step

34 22 —	52 31 —	78 94 —	64 57 —	Compound multiplication, 2 figures in multiplicand and multiplier. Two examples; no carrying. Two examples; carrying.

9th step

80 97 —	60 84 —	79 30 —	56 90 —	Compound multiplication, 2 figures in multiplicand and multiplier. '0' difficulties; carrying.

10th step

90 90 —	8460 600 —	80 100 —	1000 70 —	Extension of '0' difficulties.

11th step

483 59 —	540 75 —	870 64 —	605 29 —	Compound multiplication, 3 figures in multiplicand; carrying.

12th step

408 37 —	976 78 —	206 50 —	607 60 —	Compound multiplication, 3 figures in multiplicand, tens figure '0'; carrying.

13th step

612 517	706 309	338 430	3 figures in multiplicand and in multiplier.

14th step

7651 301	7080 605	4 figures in multiplicand, 3 figures in multiplier.

The test takes longer than preceding ones and should be taken in two parts; the examples on p. 9 (Test 8A) of the test booklet at one testing and those on p. 10 (Test 8B) at another testing.

Test 9. *Graded Division*

This test consists of eleven steps of four examples each, *i.e.* forty-four simple division sums in all, involving the use of divisors from 2 to 12. Adequate attention has been paid to the main zero difficulties that occur in simple division. Examples are arranged four in a line, *i.e.* one step per line.

1st step

4)44	2)84	3)96	6)666	Divisor is contained an even number of times in every figure of the dividend; no carrying; no remainders.

2nd step

2)682	4)844	3)696	2)2426	Same as step 1, but with larger numbers; no carrying; no remainders.

3rd step

3)906	2)806	4)840	3)690	'0' at end or in middle of dividend; no carrying; no remainders.

4th step

4)800	3)900	6)600	8)1600	Double '0' at end of dividend; noughts in quotient; no carrying; no remainders.

5th step

5)$\overline{1515}$	7)$\overline{6342}$	9)$\overline{8136}$	8)$\overline{4856}$	Divisor is not contained in 3rd figure of dividend (giving nought in quotient), but it is contained in last 2 figures of dividend; no carrying; no remainders.

6th step

4)$\overline{27}$	8)$\overline{53}$	9)$\overline{80}$	7)$\overline{61}$	Dividends under 100; remainders.

7th step

7)$\overline{50}$	4)$\overline{97}$	9)$\overline{89}$	6)$\overline{57}$	Similar to step 6.

8th step

5)$\overline{156}$	4)$\overline{167}$	7)$\overline{149}$	6)$\overline{128}$	3-figure dividends; no carrying; remainders.

9th step

9)$\overline{372}$	12)$\overline{759}$	8)$\overline{697}$	11)$\overline{569}$	3-figure dividends; larger divisors; carrying; remainders.

10th step

3)$\overline{248}$	6)$\overline{745}$	5)$\overline{3462}$	7)$\overline{5573}$	Larger dividends; carrying; remainders.

11th step

8)$\overline{29643}$	5)$\overline{25357}$	7)$\overline{49010}$	9)$\overline{307868}$	5- or 6-figure dividends; '0' difficulties; carrying; remainders.

Test 10. *Long Division*

Tests 10 and 11 both deal with the most difficult process in elementary arithmetic, namely long division. Naturally the possible number of examples in relatively simple long division is exceedingly great, but an attempt has been made to compile two tests which will give a fairly comprehensive survey of the major long division difficulties.[1] Four examples are allotted to each step, and each step occupies a single line in the booklet.

1st step

$20\overline{)40}$	$33\overline{)99}$	$43\overline{)86}$	$21\overline{)84}$	The simplest step in long division; the quotient, which consists of one figure, is apparent at sight from the nature of the figures in divisor and dividend; no remainders.

2nd step

$23\overline{)48}$	$32\overline{)99}$	$24\overline{)49}$	$20\overline{)86}$	This step is only a very little different from step 1; the quotient is apparent from the nature of the first figures of divisor and dividend, but there is a remainder.

3rd step

$43\overline{)89}$	$20\overline{)97}$	$22\overline{)56}$	$31\overline{)98}$	This step is a slight advance on step 2, as the quotient is not so apparent in two examples.

4th step

$33\overline{)74}$	$42\overline{)93}$	$23\overline{)72}$	$41\overline{)90}$	In this step the first figure of the divisor is not contained equally in the first figure of the dividend. There are single figure quotients and single figure remainders, with borrowing.

5th step

$21\overline{)126}$	$32\overline{)128}$	$41\overline{)164}$	$53\overline{)159}$	The first figure of the divisor in this step is not contained at all in the first figure of the dividend, but in the first two figures; 3-figure dividend; single figure quotient; no remainders.

[1] Sets of graded examples based on each step in short division (Test 9) and in long division (Tests 10 and 11) are provided for practice or remedial work on pp. 19-27 of *Practice in Basic Arithmetic*, Book Three.

6th step

43)$\overline{139}$	94)$\overline{189}$	71)$\overline{288}$	82)$\overline{248}$	This is similar to step 5, but with remainders.

7th step

36)$\overline{756}$	63)$\overline{1449}$	52)$\overline{1456}$	97)$\overline{3298}$	There are 4 figures in the dividend; 2 figures in the quotient; no remainders in this step.

8th step

41)$\overline{3199}$	84)$\overline{5379}$	95)$\overline{7698}$	93)$\overline{5866}$	This is similar to step 7, but has single figure remainders.

9th step

48)$\overline{3360}$	81)$\overline{4050}$	54)$\overline{2700}$	56)$\overline{2800}$	Quotients not always apparent. No remainders.

Test 11. *Long Division*

This test is a continuation of Test 10 so that the steps follow on in approximate order of difficulty from the 9th step in Test 10. Preliminary trials showed that it was better to divide the long division material into two shorter tests, but with older pupils who are dull or very backward in arithmetic it is advisable to divide this test still further by giving lines A, B and C at the first testing and D, E and F at the second testing.

1st step

36)$\overline{723}$	55)$\overline{1769}$	63)$\overline{3909}$	73)$\overline{5116}$	This step, while keeping two examples similar to those in step 8 of Test 10, introduces a '0' into the quotient of the two remaining examples and has single figure remainders.

2nd step

18)$\overline{54}$	39)$\overline{156}$	35)$\overline{210}$	26)$\overline{104}$	This step introduces trial divisors in all examples. There are single figure quotients and no remainders.

3rd step

29)261	15)115	49)366	68)615	This is an extension of step 2 in so far as more trials are required to find the first quotient figure, and there are some remainders.

4th step

35)1645	27)918	46)3012	24)984	In this step there are trial divisors, 2 figures in the quotient and no remainders in three sums.

5th step

25)11475	36)13657	78)14742	29)17632	This step introduces 3-figure quotients, one with remainder and one with a '0' in the quotient.

6th step

17)12036	79)3090	21)17659	58)46814	This step involves noughts in the quotient and some remainders.

Test 12. *Graded Mental Arithmetic*

This test is composed of forty graded examples in mental arithmetic. It provides an indication of how the pupil can handle simple mechanical material in a verbal setting. The test contains examples of common combinations of the four processes and applications of these involving money, weights and measures.

General Instructions for Giving the Tests

The twelve tests considered in detail in foregoing paragraphs are printed in a sixteen-page booklet with space provided for answers and for working figures where these are necessary. It is obvious that all the tests cannot be given on the same day, but they can be completed within a week if a testing is taken each day. The distribution of the testing should depend upon the age and abilities of the pupils; with younger pupils and with those backward in arithmetic, care should be taken to avoid fatigue and boredom. For example, with 7-year-olds it is advisable to give one of Tests 1 to 5 on alternate days, *i.e.* one day testing followed by one day without testing. With pupils of 8 or 9 years, two of Tests 1 to 5 might be taken on each of two days, reserving Test 5 for a single testing.

With young or backward testees two working periods for each of Tests 6 *to* 10 *are advisable. With tests* 8B, 10 *and* 11 *two working periods are better for all pupils up to* 11+. *Black lines in the actual test booklet indicate suitable diagnostic testing units.*[1]

In general, a more reliable assessment of arithmetical attainments is obtained if the tests are distributed over two weeks, a very short time in comparison with the extensive information gathered on individual difficulties.

Answers and working to all tests may be put in the test booklets, in which case the teacher has a comprehensive record of each pupil's achievement in the number combinations, in the four rules and in mental arithmetic. On the other hand, the answers and working to the tests may be written on papers prepared by the pupils, thereby leaving the tests intact for further use. Provision for the latter form of use has been made by means of the horizontal and vertical lettering of each test. Thus if the teacher wishes to take Test 1 in this way he asks his pupils to prepare a sheet with lettering as follows:

TEST 1

	(*a*)	(*b*)	(*c*)	(*d*)	(*e*)
A					
B					
C					
D					
E etc.					

He then allows the children to work the test, putting their results on their answer papers in the appropriate line and under the correct letter.[2]

[1] Naturally, if a time limit (see Appendix I) for a test has been set, pupils are allowed to do as many examples as they can in the given time.

[2] This method of using the tests cannot be adopted when speed plus accuracy estimates for Tests 1 to 5 are required.

Tests 1 to 5 may be taken orally, the pupils writing their answers either in the booklets or on prepared sheets. Oral administration of these tests has the advantage that a better estimate is obtained of the degree to which the combinations have become automatic responses, in so far as the speed at which the test is given prevents finger counting, dot counting and such devices. On the other hand, if the child is allowed to work silently at his own pace the testing is more in keeping with the majority of the arithmetic situations in which the pupil will be placed; furthermore it is a very easy task for the teacher to note pupils who still require considerable counting aids in all the tests.

Tests 1 to 11 may be used to obtain three somewhat different measures of the child's arithmetic achievements.

(1) The tests may be used in a purely diagnostic sense, that is, to discover as comprehensively as possible what the pupil knows and what he does not know in the number combinations, in the four rules, in the various phases of the four rules and in mental arithmetic. *Every pupil is allowed to complete as much as he can of each test in unlimited time.* Gathering of diagnostic information in this way is the primary objective for which the tests are compiled. They aim to provide a complete inventory of the child's arithmetic knowledge and hence to indicate where the gaps and deficiencies lie.

(2) The tests may also be used to estimate speed of working in the various number combinations and four rules. The time taken can be obtained by requiring each pupil to raise his hand as he finishes the test. The time taken is recorded at the top of the test paper and is afterwards compared with the table of average times for the various chronological age groups (given in the next chapter). For example, if a pupil aged $9\frac{9}{12}$ takes 7 minutes to complete Test 1 when the average time for pupils of the same age is $4\frac{1}{2}$ minutes, we have an objective estimate of his speed in adding the basic number combinations.

(3) A combined measure of accuracy and speed may be derived from the tests by setting a time limit for each.

The arithmetic ages obtained from the use of the given time limit for each test are often most helpful in indicating strengths and weaknesses, but particularly the latter, in the basic combinations and in the four processes. The arithmetic age for a testee in addition combinations (Test 1) may be compared with his arithmetic age in graded addition (Test 6); his results in subtraction combinations (Test 2) with those in graded subtraction (Test 7) and so on. In this way the teacher obtains fuller information on each pupil's arithmetical achievements with a clearer insight into the nature of his failure. But the tests also serve as a method of checking progress by repeating them (using the time limits) after a period of special practice or remedial teaching.

Special Instructions for Giving the Tests

Before pupils begin a test it is as well to see that they have all turned to the particular test to be worked: test number and page number both help in this respect. Furthermore, it is advisable to impress on pupils, particularly young ones, the nature of the process they are about to do. For example, in Test 1 we should say: 'Now you are going to work a lot of little addition—add—sums.' (Put the sign on the blackboard.) 'You will have plenty of time, but you must work quickly and carefully.' Some such similar instructions should precede each test.

Care should be taken to point out that Test 5 involves four processes.

If times are being obtained for each pupil say: 'Put up your hand as soon as you finish the test. Don't wait to look over it; put your hand up.'

It is as well, with younger pupils, to allow all to complete a test before proceeding with the next. Timing can be carried out with a watch having a second hand; time to the nearest minute is sufficient.

Marking and Scoring the Tests

With young pupils aged 7 or 8 it is advisable for the teacher to correct the tests, but with older pupils it is beneficial that they should correct their own results, in which case the teacher will read the answers (given in Appendix II) aloud slowly. Incorrect exercises should be so marked to facilitate later qualitative analysis by the teacher.

The scoring is one mark for each correct answer. The table below gives the maximum number of marks for each test.

Test	Kind	Maximum Score
1	Addition . . .	100
2	Subtraction . .	100
3	Multiplication . .	100
4	Division . . .	90
5	Miscellaneous (1-4) .	100
6	Addition . . .	58
7	Subtraction . .	56
8A & B	Multiplication . .	53
9	Division . . .	44
10	Long Division . .	36
11	Long Division . .	24
12	Mental . . .	40
	Total maximum score	801

It proves useful to record results together with any special remarks regarding the pupils' work or remedial teaching on the front page of the booklet. If the pupil is very backward in arithmetic and the tests have been used in their full diagnostic sense, as regards both accuracy and time, the results may be recorded on an additional sheet, pasted inside the test, in the form shown below.

Test	Time taken	Comparison with Norms	No. Right	Comparison with Norms	Special Difficulties	Suggestions for Remedial Work
1						
2						
3						
4						
etc.						

COEFFICIENTS OF RELIABILITY

Test	Age 9	Age 10	Age 11	Age 12
6	·97	·97	·95	·99
7	·98	·97	·96	·98
8A	·88	·91	·89	·97
9	·95	·96	·96	·97
10	—	·97	·97	·97
11	—	·96	·94	·94

The above reliability coefficients, corrected by means of the Spearman Brown formula for a test twice as long, were obtained from the scores of 100 pupils in each of the four age groups.

Reliability coefficients were also calculated by means of the test-retest technique, that is, repeating the test after an interval of time. The coefficients obtained in this way, although high, are somewhat less than those derived by the split half method, as the repetition of the test involves a slight increase in scores due to a practice effect.

SUMMARY OF THE USES OF THE TESTS

The detailed discussion in the foregoing pages clearly shows that the tests are primarily for diagnosing difficulties in arithmetic. They provide the class teacher with an instrument that is both scientific and systematic, and hence are of paramount value, not only with pupils backward in arithmetic, but with all children who are engaged in consolidating the fundamental processes and their applications. Extensive use of the tests in different departments during the two years devoted to preliminary testing shows that they can be employed profitably for a variety of purposes.

(*a*) The tests are suitable for estimating accuracy in the fundamental combinations amongst pupils in infant classes before their transfer to junior classes.

(*b*) The tests will provide useful information concerning all pupils in junior schools.

(*c*) The tests are invaluable as a guide to both the attainments and the difficulties of dull pupils. They indicate starting-points and curriculum objectives for the teacher.

(*d*) With children backward in arithmetic the tests isolate with certainty individual difficulties and reveal the lines along which remedial teaching should proceed.

(*e*) Pupils coming to a school from another area can be given the tests to ascertain where they shall be placed with regard to future arithmetic teaching.

(*f*) The tests can be used as a basis for dividing pupils into arithmetic sets, where this method of organisation is used.

(*g*) Groups of pupils who are to be transferred to post-primary school can be tested prior to their final term in the junior school and given practice in the processes where weaknesses are still displayed.

(*h*) Testing of all pupils in a secondary modern school, but particularly the more backward ones, provides much useful information for teachers and prevents further work being attempted where the fundamentals are still not sufficiently well known.

Having examined the tests in detail and considered their administration, marking and uses, we now pass to an interpretation of the results obtained from them.

CHAPTER VII

INTERPRETATION OF THE RESULTS

BEFORE considering the interpretation of the results of the tests it cannot be too strongly emphasised that they are essentially for diagnostic purposes. They are constructed according to definite principles in order to detect difficulties in arithmetic amongst ordinary primary school pupils. It is on the qualitative not the quantitative side that they yield most information. It is one aim to discover how well a pupil can do a test or, conversely, how backward he is, but it is another and more important aim to know exactly the nature of any difficulties or gaps in his work and why he is backward in certain phases of a subject. It is this latter form of information that the diagnostic test is able to provide.

Naturally all interpretation should embrace, to some extent, both qualitative and quantitative aspects, so that, although the diagnostic test emphasises qualitative examination, it makes some provision for quantitative estimates. The figures given in the tables of averages enable separate assessments for speed and for accuracy to be made.

The number of examples correctly worked by any group of children in the various tests, and the time taken by each pupil to complete each test, can be easily ascertained. The value of such data is then enhanced if individual scores and times are compared with those of other pupils of similar ages. Such a comparison gives some idea of the pupil's achievements in terms of normal standards. This quantitative interpretation is made possible by the use of tables of averages which have been compiled on the basis of the average number of examples correct and the average times taken by each of the age groups 8 to 13 years—age being considered as age last birthday. These averages, which must only be considered as approximations, have been calculated for normal pupils aged 8 to 13 years.

There are, however a number of points to be noted before use of the tables can be considered in detail.

Firstly, no averages were calculated for the 7-year-old groups, for it is of little benefit to obtain at that stage a quantitative assessment of such pupils' arithmetical attainments. It is much more profitable to determine the exact nature of the progress they have made in the fundamental number combinations and the difficulties they have so far encountered than to discover how much they have learnt, that is, from a purely quantitative standard of accuracy and speed. For most 7-year-old pupils the most useful material is found in Tests 1 to 4 and in the first three or four steps of Tests 6, 7, 8A and 9.

Secondly, no averages for items correct in unlimited time are given for Tests 1 to 5. Since there is no time limit for the tests and the material is relatively easy, there is little to discriminate the normal 8-year-old from the normal 12-year-old on actual number right. The primary purpose of the test is to reveal individual difficulties in particular number combinations or to expose a general weakness in a particular process. Naturally there are definite differences from age group to age group in the times taken to complete these tests, and hence average times for each group are given.

Thirdly, in so far as it is for all pupils aged 8 to 13 years, irrespective of type of school or level of intelligence, that the diagnostic tests are intended, the averages for times and scores have been compiled from results obtained within several different types of schools in order to obtain a representative set of results. That is, results were obtained from normal samples of children aged 8, 9 and 10 years in junior schools and from children aged 11, 12 and 13 years in secondary modern schools, with the addition at these latter ages (11+ to 13+) of a just proportion of representatives who had been transferred to selective post-primary schools. All results thus apply to representative samples of pupils in each of the six age groups. In general, it was found that average scores from a normal sample of 10-year-olds in a junior school were similar to those from 11-year-olds in a secondary modern school, while 11-, 12- and 13-year-old scores in a secondary modern school differed from those of the total sample (*i.e.* secondary modern school pupils plus a proportion of pupils from other secondary schools) by 3-19 marks in the various tests.[1]

It will thus be of interest for teachers to compare results from secondary modern schools or from 'C' and 'D' classes in non-selective secondary schools with the tabulated averages which represent a normal sample of the school population.

It will be noted that, as the tests are diagnostic and hence no time limits are used, the average numbers of sums correct amongst the upper-age groups do not show, in some tests, very marked differences from group to group.

The average number of sums correct *in unlimited time* together with the backwardness levels for each of the age groups 8 to 13 years are given in the following tables.

TABLE I

TEST 6. GRADED ADDITION

Number of Sums Correct in Unlimited Time

Age	Average no. correct	Weakness indicated if below
8	50	43
9	54	48
10	55	50
11	56	51
12	57	52
13	57	53

TABLE II

TEST 7. GRADED SUBTRACTION

Number of Sums Correct in Unlimited Time

Age	Average no. correct	Weakness indicated if below
8	44	31
9	48	36
10	52	42
11	54	48
12	55	50
13	55	52

[1] Actually the differences are 4-19 marks in Tests 1-5, with an average difference of 11 marks, and 3-9 marks in Tests 6-12, with an average difference of 6 marks.

TABLE III

TEST 8A AND B. GRADED MULTIPLICATION

Number of Sums Correct in Unlimited Time

Age	Average no. correct	Weakness indicated if below
8	20	18
9	37	26
10	43	32
11	46	38
12	50	47
13	51	49

TABLE IV

TEST 9. GRADED DIVISION

Number of Sums Correct in Unlimited Time

Age	Average no. correct	Weakness indicated if below
8	21	12
9	37	28
10	39	31
11	41	36
12	43	39
13	43	41

TABLE V

TEST 10. LONG DIVISION (EASY STEPS)

Number of Sums Correct in Unlimited Time

Age	Average no. correct	Weakness indicated if below
8	..	..
9	20	12
10	27	18
11	30	21
12	34	30
13	35	32

TABLE VI

TEST 11. LONG DIVISION (HARDER STEPS)

Number of Sums Correct in Unlimited Time

Age	Average no. correct	Weakness indicated if below
8	..	..
9	..	..
10	18	12
11	20	15
12	21	17
13	22	19

TABLE VII

TEST 12. GRADED MENTAL ARITHMETIC

Number of Sums Correct in Unlimited Time

Age	Average no. correct	Weakness indicated if below
8	12	6
9	19	13
10	30	24
11	34	28
12	36	31
13	37	33

It must be emphasised that the average scores given in Tables I to VII are to be regarded only as approximate minima around which pupils of particular ages should be grouped. The scores must not, in any sense, be regarded as final objectives; they simply represent a normal level of accuracy in fundamental processes irrespective of speed. Pupils may be slow, but this will be detected if a time limit is set or if the time for completion of the test is taken.

To facilitate the selection of pupils who show weakness in particular processes, minimum levels have been calculated from the spread of all scores. If a pupil, with unlimited time at his disposal, fails to reach the figure set down in the third column of each table, then he must be considered as weak in the particular process and should receive individual assistance.

Averages of Times Taken for Each Test

The time that each pupil took to complete each test was obtained, and from the data averages were calculated. Thus the figures given on pp. 118-21 represent the average times in which pupils between the ages of 8 and 13 years can be expected *to complete* the various tests. The figures indicate speed of working irrespective of accuracy.

TABLE VIII

Test 1. Addition

(100 Basic Combinations)

Average Times in Minutes taken to Complete the Test

Age	Average time taken	Weakness in speed indicated if A.T. is greater than
8	8	11
9	6	8
10	4	6
11	4	6
12	3·5	4·5
13	3	4

TABLE IX

Test 2. Subtraction

(100 Basic Combinations)

Average Times in Minutes taken to Complete the Test

Age	Average time taken	Weakness in speed indicated if A.T. is greater than
8	11	17
9	8	12
10	6	8
11	5	7·5
12	4	6
13	3·5	5

TABLE X

TEST 3. MULTIPLICATION

(100 Basic Combinations)

Average Times in Minutes taken to Complete the Test

Age	Average time taken	Weakness in speed indicated if A.T. is greater than
8	9	16
9	6	12
10	4	7
11	4	6
12	3·5	5
13	3	4

TABLE XI

TEST 4. DIVISION

(90 Basic Combinations)

Average Times in Minutes taken to Complete the Test

Age	Average time taken	Weakness in speed indicated if A.T. is greater than
8	13	21
9	9	14
10	6	10
11	5	9
12	4	7
13	3	5

TABLE XII

TEST 5. MISCELLANEOUS

(100 Hardest Combinations in Four Rules)

Average Times in Minutes taken to Complete the Test

Age	Average time taken	Weakness in speed indicated if A.T. is greater than
8	16	23
9	13	18
10	8	12
11	7	11
12	6	9
13	5	8

TABLE XIII

TEST 6. GRADED ADDITION

Average Times in Minutes taken to Complete the Test

Age	Average time taken	Weakness in speed indicated if A.T. is greater than
8	18	25
9	11	16
10	9	13
11	9	13
12	7	10
13	6	9

TABLE XIV

TEST 7. GRADED SUBTRACTION

Average Times in Minutes taken to Complete the Test

Age	Average time taken	Weakness in speed indicated if A.T. is greater than
8	19	27
9	13	19
10	10	15
11	9	13
12	7	10
13	6	9

TABLE XV

TEST 8A AND B. GRADED MULTIPLICATION

Average Times in Minutes taken to Complete the Test

Age	Average time taken	Weakness in speed indicated if A.T. is greater than
8	..	..
9	30	40
10	25	33
11	24	30
12	20	26
13	15	21

TABLE XVI

TEST 9. GRADED DIVISION

Average Times in Minutes taken to Complete the Test

Age	Average time taken	Weakness in speed indicated if A.T. is greater than
8	26	35
9	14	20
10	9	13
11	8	12
12	6	9
13	5	8

TABLE XVII

TEST 10. LONG DIVISION (EASY STEPS)

Average Times in Minutes taken to Complete the Test

Age	Average time taken	Weakness in speed indicated if A.T. is greater than
8	33	46
9	28	40
10	21	30
11	19	27
12	15	22
13	11	18

TABLE XVIII

TEST 11. LONG DIVISION (HARDER STEPS)

Average Times in Minutes taken to Complete the Test

Age	Average time taken	Weakness in speed indicated if A.T. is greater than
8	..	..
9	..	..
10	25	34
11	24	31
12	22	28
13	19	26

Average Scores for Accuracy in Given Times

Previous tables have given separate estimates of accuracy in unlimited time (Tables I-VII) and of speed, irrespective of accuracy (Tables VIII-XVIII), for the various diagnostic tests, but what is most useful to the teacher is a combined estimate of accuracy and speed. Most class teachers wish to know how the achievements of their pupils in graded tests of the four processes compare with those of other pupils of similar ages under similar conditions. This comparison can be made by using the test booklet and by observing the following times for Tests 6 to 12:

Test 6, 6 minutes; Test 7, 6 minutes; Test 8A, 7 minutes; Test 8B, 7 minutes; Test 9, 5 minutes; Test 10, 9 minutes; Test 11, 15 minutes; Test 12, 10 minutes.

Naturally all the tests are not given to pupils at one testing, nor is it necessary to give all tests to all pupils. For pupils of 7+ and 8+ it is sufficient to give Tests 6, 7, 8A and 9 on separate days. For normal pupils of 9+ and over, the work can be done in 3 testing units on separate days:

Unit 1, Tests 6, 7, 8A (19 minutes); *Unit* 2, Tests 8B, 9, 10 (21 minutes); *Unit* 3, Tests 11 and 12 (25 minutes).

Allow a break of 2 or 3 minutes between each test, and keep strictly to the given times. Scores are: 1 mark for each sum correct—no partial credits are allowed. Scores and corresponding arithmetic ages[1] from 2,400 pupils (fully representative samples), between the ages of 7 and 15, under the given times and conditions are set out in Appendix I, pages 186-89.

Tests 6 to 12 can thus be used as standardised attainment tests to provide a basis for comparing, in arithmetical achievements, pupils of similar ages. Teachers will also find the scores useful for speeding up accuracy in the fundamentals. The test can be repeated at intervals and progress checked by comparing scores.

Arithmetic ages in the various arithmetical processes may

[1] Norms for children in Scottish schools have been provided by Dr P. Vernon in *The Scottish Educational Journal*, 9th February, 1940.

be obtained from the tables on pages 186-89. For example, Pupil A, Chron. Age 11, scores 44 on Test 6 and 25 on Test 7. Thus his arithmetic age for graded addition is 11 years 1 month, but his arithmetic age for graded subtraction is only 9 years 9 months, a difference of 16 months—sufficiently great to warrant special remedial help with subtraction.

Schedules of Common Errors

The diagnostic test will reveal exactly the amount known by each pupil in the various processes and will indicate the point at which failure, if any, occurs. But this is only part of a full diagnostic programme, for the nature of the errors made and why they are made should be known. In this part of the diagnosis considerable help can be obtained by familiarising ourselves with the common types of errors. Hence schedules of common errors in addition, subtraction, multiplication and division have been compiled from results of the diagnostic tests, and the types of these errors, in approximate order of frequency, are listed in the sections that follow.

The teacher will find it profitable to take with his most backward pupils an oral examination of their incorrect examples, keeping in mind the schedule of errors in the process under consideration. Causes of the errors are also indicated in the schedules.

Schedule A

Common Errors in Addition

A. 1. *Errors in combinations:*

Example (*a*)	94 83 76 59 — 311	Error: 18+4=21. Here the error was a temporary lapse in accuracy. Combination is really known.
Example (*b*)	57 59 — 117	Error: 9+7=17. This proves to be an habitual error for this child, as revealed by oral testing and by the results of Test 1. Needs individual practice in plenty of small sums involving 9+7 and 7+9.

A. 2. *Omitted carrying figure:*

Example (*a*)

```
  39
  48
  --
  77
```

Error: omitted to carry 1.
Here pupil omits carrying number very frequently. Obviously carrying is not an automatic process. Needs practice from beginning with simple 'carrying' examples.

Example (*b*)

```
     3
    81
    19
   827
    94
  ----
  1004
```

Error: omitted to carry 2.
Here error due to fact that pupil adds carrying number in whenever it makes a complete 10; therefore it is sometimes forgotten.

A. 3. *Carried wrong number:*

Example

```
   94
   83
   76
   59
  ---
  302
```

Error: carried 1 instead of 2.
More exercises needed in column addition with a variety of carrying numbers.

A. 4. *Added in numbers from other column:*

Example

```
     3
    81
    19
   827
    94
  ----
  1054
```

Error: added in 3 again in tens column.
This is sometimes due to bad setting out of sums, sometimes to lapse of attention.

A. 5. *Added in carrying number twice:*

Example

```
   28
  103
  784
    9
  ---
  944
```

Error: added in 2 twice in tens column.
This is due either to lack of consistency in the time at which the carrying number is added or to retracing steps.

A. 6. *Omitted number or numbers from column:*

Example

```
   951
   382
   467
   539
   196
  ----
  2455
```

Error: omitted 8 in adding.
This is due to losing place in column or to irregular habits of adding. Practice needed in checking answer downwards.

Schedule B

Common Errors in Subtraction

S. 1. *Omitted to allow for borrowing:*

Example		
	786 58 — 738	Error: omitted to allow for 'borrowing', 8−5 instead of 8−6. Many of these errors appear to be due to lapses, but in the early stages of subtraction many pupils go through a period of intermittent error in this direction. Oral working of examples decreases the error.

S. 2. *Subtracted figures in top line (minuend) from those in bottom line (subtrahend):*

Example		
	316 27 — 311	Error: 7−6 and 2−1 instead of 6−7, etc. Sometimes this is due to general ignorance of subtraction process, sometimes to the nature of the figures in the two lines, sometimes to bad teaching. Thus oral examination of one group of backward pupils in a junior school showed that in such an example as the above they would say, '6 take away 7', that is, the top line mentioned first, with the result that in suggestible situations the wrong figures were subtracted.

S. 3. *Subtraction of like numbers in minuend and subtrahend:*

Example (*a*)	38 8 — 38	Error: 8−8=8. Drill required on actual combinations of subtracting like numbers.
Example (*b*)	250 49 — 211	Error: 5−5=1.

S. 4. *Subtraction of '0' from a digit or a digit from '0':*

Example (*a*)	890 889 — 9	Error: 0−9=9. This is a common error—that of writing in the answer the number to be subtracted from zero.

Example (*b*)

```
 607
 318
 ---
 319
```

In general the difficulty seems to be one of adding 10 to 0. The child experiences difficulty in seeing that $10-0=10$, or in then using the 10 from which to subtract.

Example (*c*)

```
 80
 57
 --
 30
```

S. 5. *Added instead of subtracting:*

Example

```
 387
 196
 ---
 421
```

S. 6. *'Paying back' to the subtrahend when there was no 'borrowing':*

Example

```
 987
 832
 ---
 145
```

Error: $8-4$ instead of $8-3$. Give series of examples alternating 'borrowing' and no 'borrowing'.

Schedule C

Common Errors in Multiplication

M. 1. *Errors in tables:*

Example

```
  7004
     8
 -----
 48034
```

Errors: $4\times8=34$, $7\times8=48$. This error far outweighs any other in multiplication. It points to the difficulty and the need of making the basic multiplication facts absolutely automatic, through drill and games.

M. 2. *Errors in 'carrying' numbers:*

Example (*a*)

```
  874615
       9
 -------
 7871495
```

Error: omitted to carry 4. Requires plenty of short sums involving a variety of 'carrying'.

Example (*b*)

```
   56
   90
 ----
 4940
```

Error: carried wrong number. In this case the number written down in the answer was carried.

Example (*c*)

```
  95347
      6
 ------
 572182
```

Error: $18+2=21$. Requires practice in combinations involving adding in multiplication.

M. 3. *Errors in noughts in multiplier or multiplicand:*

Example (*a*)

```
 400
   8
----
3288
```

Error: $8 \times 0 = 8$.

Example (*b*)

```
  90
  90
----
8100
  90
----
8190
```

Error: $90 \times 0 = 90$.

Example (*c*)

```
 80
100
---
800
 80
 80
---
960
```

Errors: position of figures (800 for 8000) and $80 \times 0 = 80$.

Example (*d*)

```
  206
   50
-----
10000
```

Error: omitted to carry figure 3 after multiplying 0 by 5.

M. 4. *Errors in position of figures:*

Example (*a*). Starting to multiply from the right:

```
 34
 22
---
 68
 68
---
136
```

Example (*b*). Starting to multiply from the left:

```
 52
 31
---
156
 52
---
208
```

Schedule D

Common Errors in Division

D. 1. *Errors in basic combinations:*

Example (*a*)	411 9)2799	Error: 27÷9=4. Requires speed practice in division combinations, with and without remainders.
Example (*b*)	9 r. 7 9)89	Error: 89−81=7.

D. 2. *Omitted to carry figure:*

Example	32 4)138	Error: omitted to carry 1.

D. 3. *Remainder larger than divisor:*

Example	6 r. 8 7)50	Error: 7×6 instead of 7×7. Needs practice with basic combinations involving remainders.

D. 4. *Omitted* '0' *from quotient:*

Example (*a*)	701 r. 3 7)49010
Example (*b*)	375 r. 3 8)29643

D. 5. *Carried wrong number:*

Example	632 r. 2 5)3462	Error: 6×5=30, 34−30=4, then carried 1 instead of 4.

D. 6. *Used same number in dividend twice:*

Example	3785 r. 3 8)29643	Error: 6 used in dividing into 56 and again to divide into 64; 4 used to divide into 64 and again to divide into 43.

Summary of Diagnostic Information provided by the Tests

Application of the Diagnostic Tests will reveal with different children a wide range of arithmetical knowledge and an equally wide range of difficulties. In general the nature of these difficulties revealed by the pupils may be grouped under one or other of four headings.

Group 1

Pupils in this group make a large number of errors in Diagnostic Tests 1 *to* 4 and are extremely slow and inaccurate in responding to the basic combinations. In almost all cases these children have not had sufficient experience of numbers in a concrete form. They have not counted, added, shared and so on with a variety of materials (beads, blocks, counters etc.) in different situations, so that they have not been able to form stable number concepts. For the variety and extent of a pupil's experiences with concrete material and pictorial representations of it largely determine the speed and efficiency shown by him in forming his early number concepts; in understanding, for example, that 4 really means a number of different things—that it is 4 units, that it is 1 more than 3, that it is 1 less than 5, that it is a group of 4 units made up of 3+1 or 1+3 units or 2+2 units. Such pupils cannot, for example, respond accurately to 5+4 or 11−3 because they have no adequate idea of what 11, 5, 4 and 3 really mean.

John F. was an example of this group of pupils. He laboriously worked through each of the Diagnostic Tests 1 to 4, only to register 57, 64, 85 and 88 errors in the tests respectively. Even finger counting and dot making did not seem to help him very much because he was so unsure of himself.

What these children obviously need is practice in working the basic number combinations in addition and subtraction up to 20 with the aid of *concrete counters.* Much of this could take the form of group games. Firstly, they need to work through Sets 1, 2, 3, 4 in Book One of *Practice in Basic Arithmetic, using concrete material.* They should not do any sums, as such, until they have strengthened their number concepts through much working with concrete materials. (For fuller discussion of the difficulties of these pupils see Chapter VIII.)

Group 2

These pupils are accurate in their work but are so slow that in output they do not complete in similar time more than about one half of the amount done by other pupils of similar chronological age.

These children often still require help from concrete material when doing their basic combinations. They can respond accurately to 7+6 or 13−7 provided they can make dots or use their fingers. They require a combination of games with concrete counters to step up their responses, and quick practice with the material in Book One of *Practice in Basic Arithmetic*. As an example I quote the results of Freda A. (I.Q. 105), C.A. $9\frac{6}{12}$. In the first four Diagnostic Tests she obtained the following scores and equivalent arithmetic ages:

	Score	Arithmetic Age Years	Arithmetic Age Months
Test 1	34	7	8
Test 2	30	7	6
Test 3	20	7	5
Test 4	12	7	5

Her scores on Tests 6, 7, 8A and 9 were similarly low, due mainly, of course, to her slowness in responding to the various number combinations involved in the different sums.

Group 3

In the third group of pupils are those who have a fairly good working accuracy in the fundamental number combinations, but who reveal in their Diagnostic Test results certain special errors.

Thus one boy of 10 always made an error in 7+8 and 8+7, to which he gave the response of 13. He was helped by working a set of sums which involved 8+7, 7+8, 15−7 and 15−8 in a variety of situations.

Other children, for example, while they are effective in their addition and subtraction, may show constant errors in '0' difficulties (8×0=8 or 7−0=0) or in like figures.

Group 4

This is a group of pupils whose Diagnostic Test results show, not weakness in the basic number combinations, but insufficient knowledge of the steps in the four processes.

Not infrequently the gaps or unconsolidated knowledge of these pupils may be due to a combination of factors such as absence from or frequent change of school (discussed in Chapter IV), but at times it is the derivative of ineffective teaching through which pupils have not consolidated each successive step in a process by working a sufficient number of graded examples. Sometimes this has been a natural resultant from an attempt to cover a too extensive syllabus, or, what is more likely, to cover it too quickly to prepare children for the inevitable secondary school entrance examination. They have been hurried along too quickly, so they have not really understood what they have been doing in some aspects of the four rules.

A detailed discussion of the steps in remedial teaching for these four groups and for a fifth group, the innately dull children, is given in Chapters VIII and IX.

CHAPTER VIII

REMEDIAL TEACHING IN ARITHMETIC (FIRST STAGES)

EARLIER sections in this book dealt with the use of diagnostic tests to reveal children's arithmetical difficulties and Chapter VII contained a summary of the kind of information we might expect from applying the tests, in whole or in part, to backward arithmeticians. However, diagnosis and subsequent clarification are only part of the programme in helping those failing in their school work, and for the psychologist and the teacher the remedial measures that follow diagnosis are often the more exacting and more extensive part of the programme.

The pupil who has made normal progress in arithmetic over say three, four or more years, has gone on from stage to stage in a step by step manner—in other words his successful attainment at 9, or 10, or 11 years of age represents successful learning of many interdependent items of knowledge, each one strengthening his ability in a cumulative way. Similarly failure has its cumulative effect, and the pupil of, say, 9, 10 or 11 who is two or three years behind the others in arithmetic, has many gaps and unconsolidated steps in his arithmetic.

FIVE GROUPS OF PUPILS BACKWARD IN ARITHMETIC

It is for this reason that remedial work for those who have failed in arithmetic must be planned in a systematic and comprehensive way. Although each pupil's difficulties should be treated, as far as possible, on an individual basis, yet it is convenient to consider those backward in arithmetic in five groups.

These are—

(1) pupils who make a large number of errors in the basic number combinations as revealed in their results in diagnostic tests 1 to 4;

(2) pupils who are accurate in their work but who are so slow that in output they do not complete, in similar time, more than about one half of the amount done by other pupils of similar chronological age;

(3) those who have a fairly good working accuracy in the fundamental number combinations but who reveal in their diagnostic test results certain individual errors;

(4) those whose diagnostic test results show, not weakness in the basic number combinations, but insufficient knowledge of the steps in the four processes;

(5) dull and less able pupils whose limitations in intelligence make them inaccurate and slow in their arithmetic when judged by normal standards.

How then can we help these various groups of children who experience difficulty in their arithmetic lessons? Obviously some of them require remedial teaching of a special kind to overcome their particular difficulties, but all of them need the same kind of sympathetic, encouraging approach to produce early success and to dissipate the effects of past failure. For most of them this success will come from the systematic and frequent use in the early stages of scientifically compiled and carefully graded remedial material. This approach, using scientifically prepared material, and supplemented by play-way methods, will, in almost all instances, bring marked improvement. What perhaps will be most useful to those working with children backward in arithmetic, whether it be the psychologist in the Child Guidance Clinic or the Remedial Education Centre, the teacher in the special class or adjustment group, or the teacher with backward pupils in a normal class, is to set out the steps and remedial materials applicable to each group.

Group 1. Extreme Weakness in Number Combinations

As was pointed out earlier, these children have not formed adequate number concepts and therefore should discontinue working sums with figures in abstract form, which as yet do not convey to them adequate concepts of their unit and group values. They need an intensive period of using concrete material of varied kinds really to understand that, for example, 5 means five single units, that it also means 2+2+1, 4+1, 3+2, 2+3, and so on. In other words, they need to be turned back as a first step to further experiences with the kind of apparatus that is now so common in a modern infant classroom. To begin with, such pupils should deal only with addition and subtraction in their new start. For them it is better to postpone multiplication and division until some facility is reached in the other two processes. We have found that the work most effectively proceeds in four stages:

Stage A: Pupils are given an opportunity to consolidate their number concepts up to 20 *by using a variety of concrete material.*

The point at which one starts in this consolidation or re-education must depend upon the degree of backwardness, the age and the intelligence of the child. With a backward, slow-learning pupil of 8 I would suggest that the remedial work should start from the beginning by allowing the pupil to discover for himself the number relationships up to 5. He may be given 5 cotton reels or blocks and be asked to write out all the different groups he can discover: 3 blocks+2 blocks=5 blocks (3+2=5), and so on. In the next step he works through combinations of numbers up to 10, then to 15 and finally up to 20. Throughout the work it is essential to lead these backward children to see that addition simply means putting things together, that if we have 7 pennies in one place and 12 in another, we have 19 pennies when we put them together, that if we have 8 sheep and 12 cows we have 20 animals, and so on.

With an older, very backward arithmetician, aged say 10½, of about average intelligence, we need not start at this point but could let him work out all the number combinations up to 10 with concrete material in the form of counters.[1]

It is imperative to realise that many of the backward pupils in this first group have been unable to make progress because they have not had sufficient experience of the number facts in meaningful situations. For them repetition or drill has been ineffective because it has not been based on understanding. They have not really learnt, for example, to add 7 things and 5 things, to take away 4 things from 11 things, and so have not been able to understand and apply the abstract forms of $7+5$ and $11-4$ and so on. Constantly we should bear in mind the point emphasised by Adams: 'One of the main impediments in schools to a treatment of the background of arithmetical processes before embarking on the teaching of the written processes themselves is the isolation of arithmetic from the rest of school life.'[2]

With younger or duller pupils, it is possible to stabilise their elementary number knowledge by using a series of *flash cards* carrying dots, in any of the groupings shown on page 136.

Children place figures alongside a series of flash cards up to 20, or conversely place cards alongside numbers. For numbers beyond 10 two cards are used; thus 17 is represented by the 10 card and the 7 card.

Any one of the three accepted forms of grouping of dots as shown overleaf may be used.

It is probably advisable to select one form of grouping and to keep to it throughout the remedial work with cards. The question is sometimes asked whether children recognise the pattern (or gestalt) or the separate dots. The evidence would appear to be that to begin with children learn by the separate dots and then gradually remember by patterns, but the speed at which this takes place is dependent on intelligence and other factors.

[1] Philip and Tacey, 69-79 Fulham High Street, London, can supply at moderate cost a wide variety of suitable counters. They have wooden beads, cubic, round or cylindrical in shape, boxes of 100 counters of button type in different colours, and plastic counters of various kinds, all useful to remedial teachers or teachers of opportunity or special classes.

[2] L. D. Adams, *A Background to Primary School Mathematics*, p. 70

Grouping by Twos (Montessori grouping)

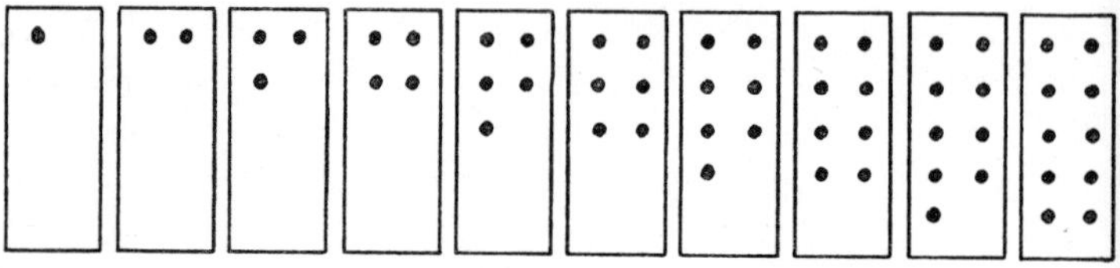

Grouping by Threes

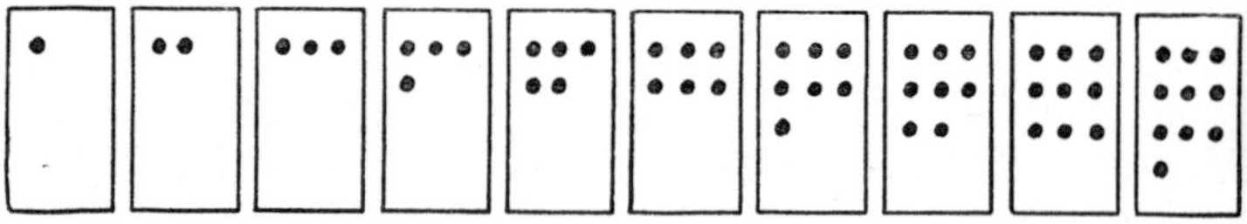

Domino or Fives Grouping

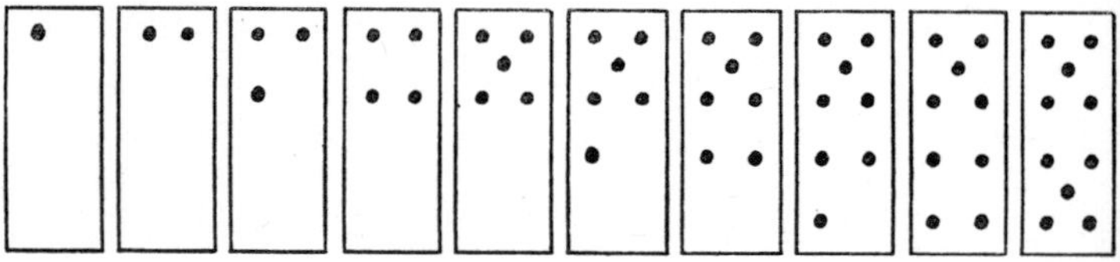

While the backward arithmetician is establishing his number concepts through experiences with the concrete, it is sometimes advisable (depending again on his age and the degree of his backwardness) to give him each day, or at times in the week, periods of activity work that will enable him to assimilate concepts of shape, size, length, weight, capacity, time, etc. by using materials that will help him to build up an arithmetic vocabulary for later work. He thus needs to be sure of terms like longer, shorter, half as long, high, short, higher, as many as, less than, more than, heavier, lighter, smaller, bigger, as much as, half as much, etc.[1]

[1] Much useful information on the child's conception of number, on approaches to the early teaching of number that will prevent difficulties arising for pupils, and suggestions that may be effective with backward arithmeticians are given in *A Background to Primary School Mathematics*, Chapters I-V, by L. D. Adams (Oxford University Press, 1953). Also *Number*, Chapters II-VII, by Thyra Smith (Basil Blackwell, 1954)

A further development of the card[1] method of concept formation is to give pupils simple addition sums by cards, thus:

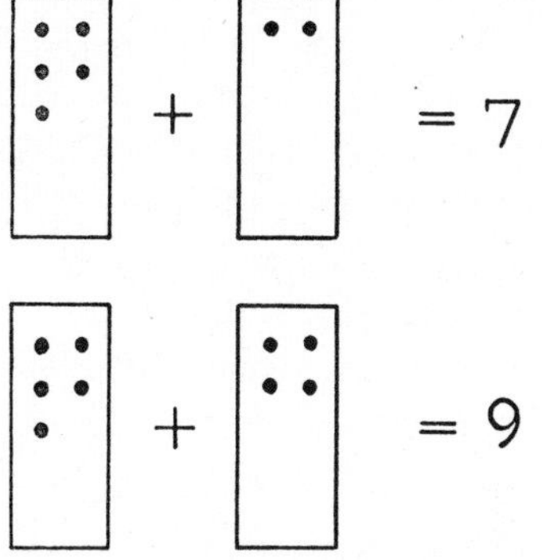

Stage B: This early work should be supplemented by a considerable amount of practice, depending on the child's needs, in adding and subtracting the basic number combinations by use of pictorial representations.

Thus, with our very backward younger children, we find it helpful to take them through Ballard's *The Child's First Number Book*[2] (29 pages) and/or *My Picture Book of Number*,[3] in which they add by means of pictorial units: 3 girls and 2 girls, 4 apples and 1 apple, 2 kites and 3 kites and so on, and do similar picture sums in subtraction.

Of particular value at this stage in remedial work with very backward or dull children is Book 2 of *Making Sure of Arithmetic* by Robert L. Morton and Merle Gray (Silver Burdett Co.).

In *The Child's Second Number Book*[4] (32 pages), pictorial representation is used for addition and subtraction up to 10, and later up to 20. A similar series, with some pictorial representation for sums, is *My First Book of Sums*[5] (32 pages), by E. G. Hume and E. C. Wheeler, and *My Book of Shops*[6]

[1] Numerous sets of cards of this kind are produced by Philip and Tacey, 69-79 Fulham High Street, London.

[2] and [4] These small books by the late Dr P. B. Ballard, a pioneer educational psychologist in Great Britain, together with a Teacher's Book, are published by the University of London Press.

[3], [5] and [6] The authors of these Kingsway Picture Arithmetics, published by Evans Bros., London, are E. G. Hume and E. C. Wheeler. See also the Teacher's Book.

(24 pages), by the same authors. This latter book, in which simple addition and subtraction facts are applied to money, is attractively illustrated.

A useful supplement for remedial work is *Help with Numbers*,[1] which contains a variety of addition and subtraction practice with concrete illustrations. It includes sums based on pictorial counting frames and has examples such as:

Draw 10 leaves on this tree.
Colour 4 leaves yellow.
How many leaves are not coloured?
Put the numbers in the box and subtract.[2]

There is also a variety of American number books that make lavish use of pictures of common objects in providing graded material on the basic number combinations. While it may not be possible for teachers in British Commonwealth countries to obtain such books in quantities, they would find it very helpful to have at least one or two sets of them. Three useful series are:

Making Sure of Arithmetic, by Robert L. Morton, Merle Gray, Elizabeth Springstun and William L. Schaaf. Illustrated books for Grades One and Two (Silver Burdett Company, 45 East 17th Street, New York 3, N.Y.)

Self Help Number Series, by MacKnight Clark and Laura Cushman (The Macmillan Co.)

Daily Life Arithmetics, by G. T. Buswell, W. A. Brownell and Leonore John (Ginn)

Thus the first and second stages of remedial work on addition and subtraction for this first group of extremely backward pupils should be to give them experience with all the basic addition combinations from $1+1$ to $9+9$ and all the basic subtraction combinations from $1-1$ to $18-9$, using extensively concrete material or pictorial representations of it. Naturally

[1] *'Help with Numbers' Dominion Workbooks. Dominion Remedial Arithmetic Exercise Book, Primary*, with *Manual of Directions*. Published by Department of Educational Research, Ontario College of Education, 370 Bloor Street West, Toronto 5

[2] Reduced in size from p. 20 of *Help with Numbers*

the order of the remedial exercises should follow an order as determined by the difficulty of the combinations.

Now there is a point of procedure to be borne in mind here. We may in the first place keep to an order of difficulty which stresses the relationships between the number combinations and so enables children to understand and later generalise in regard to the number facts; or we may use an order for remedial work based on the results of investigations to determine the relative order of difficulty of all the 100 addition facts and the 100 subtraction facts. Thus we could start with related groups or families of facts that help children to discover relationships between them. We could therefore begin with 2+1, 3+1, 4+1, 5+1, 6+1, 7+1, 8+1, 9+1, and, in order to provide for still further relationships and generalisation, we could give these facts in the reverse form of 1+2, 1+3, 1+4 and so on. We might then proceed with another related group like 2+2, 3+2, 4+2, 5+2, 6+2, 7+2, 8+2, 9+2, together with their reverse forms. It should be noted, however, that such relationship grouping may introduce combinations like 5+2 and 9+2, which prove to be slightly more difficult than combinations like 3+3 and 4+4, which appear in later relationship groups. But there is an increasing body of evidence in research journals to show that making relationships apparent to children enables them to learn their number combinations more effectively in the first place, and hence later drill or practice with the combinations arranged in a stricter order of difficulty will produce better results.[1]

It is interesting to note that in results from investigations reported by the Scottish Council for Research in Education the number combinations in addition and subtraction are, for order of teaching, divided into four groups of difficulty.[2]

[1] Those wishing to read more widely on this point might consult Chapter VI of *How to Make Arithmetic More Meaningful*, by L. J. Brueckner and F. E. Grossnickle (The John C. Winston Co.); Chapter IV of *Teaching Arithmetic in the Elementary School*, by R. L. Morton (Silver Burdett Co.) and *Fiftieth Year Book; Arithmetic in General Education*, Chapter IV by C. L. Thiele: Interrelationships in the Number System (National Council of the Teachers of Mathematics, 1941).

[2] See *Studies in Arithmetic* (University of London Press), Vol. 1, pp. 91-94 and 99-101.

Some research results indicate that the '0' combinations in addition and subtraction, which cause most errors, should be taught after children have learnt combinations not involving '0'. Other studies suggest that number facts involving '0' should be introduced as each set of number combinations is taught.

Teaching Relationship between Addition and Subtraction

One other pattern of relationships which it is most profitable to establish with children who have been failing in their arithmetic is that between related groups of numbers in addition and subtraction. Thus, most children gain considerably by having remedial work with related groups[1] such as

5+4=9	9−5=4
4+5=9	9−4=5
6+3=9	9−6=3
3+6=9	9−3=6
7+2=9	9−7=2
2+7=9	9−2=7

Practice with such groups enables them to transfer more effectively the relationships that exist between the numbers.

Two useful exercises which aid pupils to form the bond between addition and subtraction are of the following kind:

8	2	2	9	9	9	3
+ ?	+ ?	+ ?	+ ?	+ ?	+ ?	+ ?
16	11	10	11	10	18	3

0	6	6	2	8	6	1
+ ?	+ ?	+ ?	+ ?	+ ?	+ ?	+ ?
1	6	8	6	10	10	10

[1] In one investigation the percentages of children pairing each fact and its related fact (*e.g.* 11-3, 11-8; 4+5, 5+4) were obtained, and it was obvious that facts were not being taught, or at least practised, as pairs to emphasise the relationship between pairs. See *Relative Difficulties of Fundamental Facts in Arithmetic, Based on a Study of Errors made by Ontario Children*, by A. J. Phillips and H. M. Fowler (Educ. Research, Ontario College of Education, University of Toronto, 1945).

and

7	6	8	9	7	6	8
− ?	− ?	− ?	− ?	− ?	− ?	− ?
1	2	1	9	2	6	2

9	3	8	9	7	10	10
− ?	− ?	− ?	− ?	− ?	− ?	− ?
4	3	6	6	5	3	9

These examples are taken from *Practice in Basic Arithmetic* Book One.[1]

Useful information on how to develop the relationship between addition and subtraction is provided in the Teacher's Book (pages 120-35) for Book 2 of *Making Sure of Arithmetic* by Robert L. Morton and Merle Gray (Silver Burdett Co.).

Multiplication and Division Facts

Now the next step for this group of children who are very weak in their number facts is to establish firmly the idea of multiplying and dividing, and then to construct, with concrete material, the multiplication tables and the related division facts or tables. Thus, at first they will be given lessons to understand what is meant by multiplying. This may be preceded by exercises such as: Start at 2 and keep adding 2, like this—2, 4, 6, 8 . . . up to 24. *Or*: Start at 3 and keep adding 3, like this—3, 6, 9 . . . up to 36.

If necessary, for dull or very backward children this can be done with counters. They will be encouraged to write their results in this way:

$$2+0=2$$
$$2+2=4$$
$$2+2+2=6$$
$$2+2+2+2=8$$
$$2+2+2+2+2=10$$
$$2+2+2+2+2+2=12 \quad \text{etc.}$$

[1] F. J. Schonell, *Practice in Basic Arithmetic*, Book One (Oliver and Boyd, 1954), pp. 3 and 7

The pupils may thus be shown that multiplication is simply another way of assembling facts that we learn by addition, that it is a short process of repeated addition.

Then they write the table in this way :

No 2s are 0.
One 2 is 2.
Two 2s are 4.
Three 2s are 6, etc.

and then in its usual form:

$0 \times 2 = 0$
$1 \times 2 = 2$
$2 \times 2 = 4$
$3 \times 2 = 6$, etc.

Here again, slow learners might be aided to still further clarification of their ideas by encouraging them to construct each multiplication table using concrete material. Thus, with the two times table, they would form 1 group of 2, 2 groups of 2, 3 groups of 2, etc. Similar grouping of counters (or other concrete material) would be adopted for each multiplication table.

Further stabilising of the idea of repeated or cumulative adding can also arise by relating the number facts to simple money transactions. Thus in connection with the two times table it is useful to give backward pupils work with halfpennies and pennies. They know 1 penny=2 halfpennies, so a series of exercises, using actual money, can be given for them to find how many halfpennies there are in 2, 3, 4, 5 pennies, and so on. With the three times table similar exercises can be used.

Multiplication tables should be revised in their appropriate order of difficulty, namely 2, 1, 3, 5, 4, 10, 11, 6, 7, 8, 9, 12. *In all cases the table should be built up by each pupil from concrete material before any practice is given.*

From the remedial work on the multiplication facts of the two times table should stem remedial exercises associated with the related division table of 2. The pupil carries out work with concrete material, dividing numbers into groups of 2, and thus builds up the division table:

There is one 2 in 2. $2 \div 2 = 1$
There are two 2s in 4. $4 \div 2 = 2$
There are three 2s in 6. $6 \div 2 = 3$
There are four 2s in 8, etc. $8 \div 2 = 4$, etc.

It is useful to allow pupils to say over the division tables in two forms:

2 divided by $2=1$ *and* 2 into $2=1$
4 divided by $2=2$, etc. 2 into $4=2$, etc.

This stage leads on to work with pennies and halfpennies—how many two-penny pencils, two-penny sweets, etc. for two-pence, fourpence, and so on.

Further Consolidation

Remedial work in relearning and understanding the multiplication and division tables can also be further consolidated by useful exercises based on counting with concrete material. These may be of the following type:

A. Get some used match-sticks, beans, or any things which are all alike. Count out 24 of them.
Now divide your 24 into 2's. How many 2's are there?
Now divide your 24 into 3's. How many 3's are there?
Now into 4's. How many are there?
Now into 6's. How many are there?
Now count out 36 and divide them into 2's, 3's, 4's, 6's.

B. Make 30 dots on your paper, like this

Now draw lines round them in 2's, like this

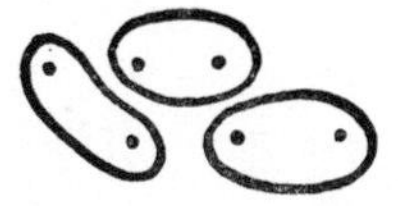

Now draw 30 more dots and mark round them in 3's. Then do the same again, but make the lines round groups of 5.

Then, last of all, make another set and mark them in groups of 6.[1]

The remedial teacher may also make use of situations in which the children line up in 2s, then in 3s, in 4s, and so on, to deal with the associated facts in the multiplication and division tables of 2, 3, 4, etc. This activity work seems to release the blockage experienced by some children in remembering multiplication and division tables.

As a preparation for division, pupils should be allowed to work through, *with counters*, the material given on pp. 13-16 of *Practice in Basic Arithmetic*, Book One. Here are two lines from this exercise:

$$\begin{array}{cccccc} 9 & 3 & 5 & 7 & 8 & 1 \\ \times\ ? & \times\ ? & \times\ ? & \times\ ? & \times\ ? & \times\ ? \\ \hline 9 & 15 & 15 & 14 & 16 & 10 \end{array}$$

$$\begin{array}{cccccc} 9 & 2 & 10 & 4 & 10 & 3 \\ \times\ ? & \times\ ? & \times\ ? & \times\ ? & \times\ ? & \times\ ? \\ \hline 18 & 18 & 10 & 12 & 20 & 12 \end{array}$$

The worked sheets of these examples should be checked by the pupils themselves from lists of answers. This provides a further method of helping them to memorise the material.

A similar procedure can be adopted with the division tables. It is then helpful for them to connect the various units in multiplication and division by working through, with counters, groups of related pairs, *e.g.*

$$\begin{array}{ll} 1\times2=2 & 2\div2=1 \\ 2\times2=4 & 4\div2=2 \\ 3\times2=6 & 6\div2=3 \\ 4\times2=8 & 8\div2=4 \\ \text{etc.} & \text{etc.} \end{array}$$

All multiplication and division tables should be so linked for slow-learning arithmeticians.

[1] Taken from pp. 37-38 of *Right from the Start Arithmetic*, Book I, by F. J. Schonell and S. H. Cracknell (Oliver and Boyd)

Stage C: Distributed Drill with the Basic Number Combinations

In the first two stages of remedial work with children very backward in arithmetic the aim is to establish understanding of what they are doing in arithmetic. Working through the basic number facts in addition, subtraction, multiplication and division with the aid of counters, although it may seem slow, is absolutely necessary if these children are to learn their number facts in the sense of forming usable number concepts. We are not in the first instance concerned with symbols but with enabling the pupils to form concepts and understand relationships that lead them to attach these correctly to symbols. Following upon understanding should come drill or practice with the number combinations. And here the aim should be to give as much practice as possible to the pupils in using the basic number facts, but with the minimum of writing and copying on their part. Distributed drill should cater for *every* child with a maximum output of practice.

The old oral form of practice with the whole class working from the blackboard, is not fully effective because it is not systematic; it does not deal scientifically with the number combinations in order of difficulty, and it does not give practice to all children. Modern methods of distributed drill in the basic number facts follow two main lines: (*a*) the use of practice books or sheets so arranged that pupils need to write the answers only; (*b*) the use of cards or games for individual or group work, so compiled as to admit of either oral or written responses and so used as to engender a spirit of play or a challenge to the pupil's desire to improve.

There is no doubt that children require opportunities for practice with the basic number facts. They need to understand them first, but equally they need systematic drill to consolidate their understanding.

Accordingly, to provide for this quick, written practice which will enable all pupils to acquire a working level of reasonable accuracy, I have prepared special material in Book One of *Practice in Basic Arithmetic*. This enables teachers to give children practice according to their individual needs; the amount and frequency of practice can be controlled. The basic number facts in addition, subtraction, multiplication and division (which for the most part form Tests 1 to 4 of the *Diagnostic Tests*) constitute the essential material which pupils must know if they are to succeed in their arithmetic. The basic number facts enter into every sum in every kind of arithmetic, oral or written, mechanical or problem. Weakness in these facts means weakness right throughout the child's arithmetic attainments.

Thus, Book One of *Practice in Basic Arithmetic*[1] contains:

Set 1:

100 Basic Addition Facts from 1+1 up to 9+9 and including '0' combinations.

Set 2:

100 Basic Addition Facts presented as missing numbers.

Set 3:

100 Basic Subtraction Facts from 1−1 up to 18−9 and including '0' combinations.

Set 4:

100 Basic Subtraction Facts presented as missing numbers.

Sets 5 *and* 6:

169 Basic Multiplication Facts from 0×0 to 12×12 (*i.e.* all the tables from 1 times to 12 times).

Sets 7 *and* 8:

157 Basic Multiplication Facts presented as missing numbers.

Sets 9 *and* 10:

156 Basic Division Facts from 0÷0 to 144÷12.

In all cases the facts are arranged in order of difficulty as determined by three different investigations.

[1] *Practice in Basic Arithmetic*, Book One (28 pages), together with Teacher's Book of instructions and suggestions, by F. J. Schonell (Oliver and Boyd, 1954)

Every pupil backward in any form of arithmetic should be given systematic practice—the amount being determined by his age and the degree of his arithmetical weakness—until his scores show improvement in accuracy and in speed, or until the particular weakness in facts or in a process is eliminated.

Each pupil should be provided with a book of examples from which he can work at his own pace. The books should not be written in and so may be used for practice over and over again. The practice material is set out as follows:

100 BASIC ADDITION FACTS

SET 1. ADDITION See how many you can do in 5 minutes

	(*a*)	(*b*)	(*c*)	(*d*)	(*e*)	(*f*)	(*g*)
A.	1 +1	0 +0	2 +2	2 +1	2 +0	3 +1	3 +3
B.	5 +5	1 +6	4 +0	4 +4	1 +7	7 +1	1 +8

etc.

SET 9. DIVISION See how many you can do in 8 minutes

	(*a*)	(*b*)	(*c*)	(*d*)	(*e*)	(*f*)
A.	2)4	5)25	2)12	2)8	2)10	2)14

etc.

The last two lines of the more difficult facts of division, which make up Set 10 are

	(*a*)	(*b*)	(*c*)	(*d*)	(*e*)	(*f*)
D.	1)11	12)96	4)48	8)88	8)96	11)132
E.	12)132	11)110	11)121	10)120	12)120	12)144

The basic addition facts are given in forward and reverse form, for a pupil may know 9+4 and yet make errors in 4+9

Furthermore all zero combinations are included in addition and subtraction. There are additional sets of practice examples providing for the addition and subtraction facts as missing numbers (*e.g.* $8+?=15$ and $11-?=3$), remedial material that assists pupils to strengthen both addition and subtraction ability. When the pupil has had practice with the addition and subtraction facts, he should be given daily practice with the 169 multiplication facts and the 156 division facts, which have been arranged in sets according to order of difficulty. A supplementary exercise to strengthen the relationship between multiplication and division presents the multiplication facts as missing numbers (*e.g.* $6\times?=30$, $9\times?=54$).

With all children, but particularly with those backward in arithmetic, short periods of daily practice give the best results. What we notice with children who come to us for remedial treatment is that this practice with small sums helps them to regain their confidence. They were failures at arithmetic and some have been censured for it, but here they are getting 'sums' right, and each day brings increased speed and accuracy.

As I have suggested in the *Teacher's Handbook*[1], the pupil's practice books may be used (1) by giving pupils prepared sheets on which to write their answers, or (2) by allowing pupils to prepare lettered pages in their pads, or (3) by providing them with a sheet of transparent paper on which to write their answers, after placing it over the page in the book. The main thing is, of course, to let children work methodically through the 10 sets of material, using 10 to 15 minutes each day for practice. I would suggest that no time limits be observed with this material for backward pupils. They require full practice on all the number combinations. Speed can come as a second stage of working. In so far as practice with this material may constitute the bulk of the remedial work for some children, up to 30 minutes' work at a session would be advisable.

The pupil's book also contains answers to the material, so that pupils should be encouraged to correct their own work.

We have found that it adds interest if pupils keep a progress

[1] For details see pp. 36-45 of the *Teacher's Handbook, Practice in Basic Arithmetic*, by F. J. Schonell (Oliver and Boyd, 1954).

card of the sets they have completed, and of the results obtained. With some this might be merely a record of the number done or the number correct. With other children it proves effective to let them record the number correct in a given time.

Stage D: Distributed Drill with Higher Decade Extensions of the Basic Number Facts

This brings us to the fourth stage in the remedial work. Having given the pupils practice in the basic number combinations in the four rules, we now need to help them extend and consolidate this knowledge in the higher decade material. The essential extensions of the basic facts consist of those higher decade forms of which the basic number facts form the core. Thus higher decade addition facts would be 24+7, 34+7 etc., or 28+3 and 38+3, of which in these examples the basic facts of 4+7 and 8+3 form the core. In division, for example, the basic division facts that the pupil has learnt are applied to forms that have remainders. Thus $4\overline{)39}$ and $8\overline{)71}$ are extended forms of the basic facts $4\overline{)36}$ and $8\overline{)64}$ respectively.

We cannot assume, however, that because our pupils show fair accuracy in all the basic number combinations they can readily and effectively transfer this knowledge to all the extended forms. And therefore it is of great help to all pupils, particularly those backward in arithmetic, to be able to give them distributed drill on all essential extended forms in addition, subtraction, multiplication and division that they are likely to use frequently in the working of their sums.

We can list all the extensions of the basic number facts, and by trying them out with children and by examining their written errors we can select those facts that require drill to consolidate them. For example, children who know 2+2 extend this knowledge without error to 12+2, 22+2, 32+2 and so on, but studies show that extensions like 6+7, which require bridging to another ten, cause errors in forms such as 26+7, 36+7 etc.

By a systematic approach to the whole problem of extensions of the basic number facts we are able to assemble lists of the most important extended forms[1] that enter into the four processes.

These essential extensions form the content of Book Two of *Practice in Basic Arithmetic* and consist of four main groups of material.

A. 240 *Higher Decade Addition Facts requiring Bridging*

This material has been selected from 360 higher decade addition combinations requiring bridging, as being those that cause most difficulty and are least likely to be transferred without specific drill. They are arranged in four sets in approximate order of difficulty.

Here are the first two lines of Set 1 of *Practice in Basic Arithmetic*, Book Two (p. 1).

HIGHER DECADE ADDITION REQUIRING BRIDGING

SET 1. See how many you can do in 8 minutes

	(*a*)	(*b*)	(*c*)	(*d*)	(*e*)	(*f*)	(*g*)	(*h*)
A.	18 +2	29 +1	69 +1	99 +1	26 +5	47 +3	19 +2	59 +1
B.	15 +5	38 +2	28 +3	89 +1	38 +3	98 +2	27 +7	85 +5

B. 168 *Higher Decade Addition Facts used in Multiplication*

Multiplication sums with two or more figures in the multiplicand often involve addition of carrying figures. Thus a sum such as 369×8 requires addition of $48+7$ and $24+5$. We can list exactly all the higher decade additions so required in multiplication, drill in which will naturally improve a pupil's speed and accuracy in multiplication.

[1] Details of how these are compiled, selected and graded for remedial work are given in *Practice in Basic Arithmetic, Teacher's Handbook*, by F. J. Schonell (Oliver and Boyd, 1954) pp. 18-20.

With children who require as much experience as possible in building up number relationships and so enabling them to arrive at generalisations teachers might prefer to teach the higher decade addition facts in families first, before giving the pupils practice with them in a mixed form.

Thus pupils would learn the 2+9 higher decade family by writing answers to the group 12+9, 22+9, 32+9, 42+9, 52+9, 62+9, 72+9, 82+9. They would be encouraged to notice that the basic fact in each combination is 2+9 and although each one increases by 10, it always ends in 1. Oral work between partners could also be used to cover all the higher decade families,[1] before gaining written practice from them by using Book Two of *Practice in Basic Arithmetic.*

The 168 Higher Decade Addition Facts used in multiplication are arranged in 3 sets in approximate order of difficulty, each with an appropriate time limit for speed plus accuracy. Backward pupils should work through them without a time limit.

C. 175 *Higher Decade Subtraction Facts used in Division*

This consists of 3 sets of material arranged in order of difficulty and covering all the important higher decade subtraction facts required in division of numbers up to 9. Backward pupils should work through these without time limits.

The last two lines of Set 1 of 60 facts are given below:

HIGHER DECADE SUBTRACTION USED IN DIVISION

SET 1. See how many you can do in 6 minutes

	(*a*)	(*b*)	(*c*)	(*d*)	(*e*)	(*f*)	(*g*)	(*h*)
G.	46 −45 — —	46 −42 — —	59 −56 — —	59 −54 — —	65 −64 — —	66 −64 — —	66 −63 — —	68 −63 — —
H.	75 −72 — —	82 −81 — —	18 −14 — —	18 −16 — —				

[1] These are given on pages 29-31 of *Practice in Basic Arithmetic, Teacher's Handbook,* by F. J. Schonell (Oliver and Boyd, 1954).

D. 336 *Division Facts with Remainders*

This remedial material consists of 8 sets of division facts selected from 537 possible division facts with remainders and arranged in approximate order of difficulty. Division is for children a difficult process, and drill with this material enables them to gain confidence in items that are constantly recurring in their arithmetic. The fact that children know their division tables is only part of the knowledge that they require, for these have to be applied to many situations where there are remainders.

For example, a pupil knows $8\overline{)56}$ or $7\overline{)49}$, and always makes correct responses to them, but when he comes across items like $8\overline{)63}$ or $7\overline{)54}$ he is inclined to make two kinds of errors. In the first place he does not readily see the quotient because each of these division facts has now gone into the next 10 above the basic fact—this may slow him up or even cause him to write the wrong quotient. Secondly, facts of this type involve remainders, and research studies show that these are a source of error for pupils. Obviously, practice with all the more important division facts with remainders will greatly improve division.

Higher Decade Division Facts in Families

Here again, teachers might wish to precede remedial practice on the division facts with remainders, arranged in order of difficulty, in which examples are in mixed form (see the sets of examples in *Practice in Basic Arithmetic*, Book Two) by an exercise, oral or written, in which they appear in their related families.

Thus the pupil would start with practice on the family of division by 2, with remainders. These are

$2\overline{)11}$ $2\overline{)13}$ $2\overline{)15}$ $2\overline{)17}$ $2\overline{)19}$

He would then proceed to practice on the family of division by 3 with remainders, which would be

$3\overline{)11}$ $3\overline{)13}$ $3\overline{)14}$ $3\overline{)16}$ $3\overline{)17}$
$3\overline{)19}$ $3\overline{)20}$ $3\overline{)22}$ $3\overline{)23}$ $3\overline{)25}$
$3\overline{)26}$ $3\overline{)28}$ $3\overline{)29}$

Preliminary practice on material of this kind is useful in building up relationships, and it forms an easy step[1] before the pupil carries out distributed practice on all the division facts with remainders. The material may be employed for oral or written work and pupils may be encouraged to form their own cards of families which can be used for quick recapitulation in groups.

Individual and Group Games with the Basic Number Facts

It may well be that the remedial teacher wishing to make an entirely fresh approach to practice or drill will take most of her remedial teaching, in the initial stages, by using material that lends itself to individual and group games. For children who have failed and felt frustrated, there is nothing like a play approach to re-kindle their interest and to build up their persistence.

I shall therefore in the following paragraphs indicate a few types of material and games[2] which, while they may be well known to infant school teachers, may not be so well known to remedial teachers at primary school level.

(*a*) *Number Combination Cards for Individual and Group Work*

The teacher, aided by the pupils, should make a large number of cards 3 inches by 2 inches and cut off the top left-hand corner of each so that the pupils will be able to keep the cards right way up. On one side of the card should be printed a number combination, and on the other side the combination with the answer, thus:

$$\begin{array}{r} 9 \\ +6 \\ \hline \\ \hline \end{array} \qquad \begin{array}{r} 9 \\ +6 \\ \hline 15 \\ \hline \end{array}$$

$$\begin{array}{r} 17 \\ -8 \\ \hline \\ \hline \end{array} \qquad \begin{array}{r} 17 \\ -8 \\ \hline 9 \\ \hline \end{array}$$

[1] All the division families, from divisor 2 to divisor 12, with their remainders, are given on pp. 32 to 35 of the Teacher's Book of *Practice in Basic Arithmetic*, by F. J. Schonell (Oliver and Boyd, 1954).

[2] These may be supplemented by other games from, for example, *Number Work in the Infant Room*, Appendix II (New Zealand Educ. Dept.).

The cards should then be arranged in sets of increasing difficulty. The number facts in each process can be similarly prepared.

These cards can be used by pupils either individually or in groups to increase accuracy and speed. For example, pupils can see how quickly they work through a set. The answer is recorded mentally and checked up by looking at the reverse side of the card, all unknown combinations being put on one side for additional drill. The value of this work lies in the interest it arouses in the pupils through the activity, and the fact that it both teaches and tests.

Once a certain degree of mastery has been attained pupils should be encouraged to test one another. Several sets can be worked through each morning in a very short time and with a very considerable improvement in accuracy in the fundamental facts in the four rules. Pairs of pupils can also play games of 'snap' with one set. A useful game for a group of three backward children is 'Pairing'. Two pupils (the players) have each a full complement of cards of the same set (for example, $9+0$, $9+1$, etc.), while a third pupil (the dealer) has a set of cards previously prepared, bearing only the answers to combinations used in the set. The players spread out their cards in rows before them thus:

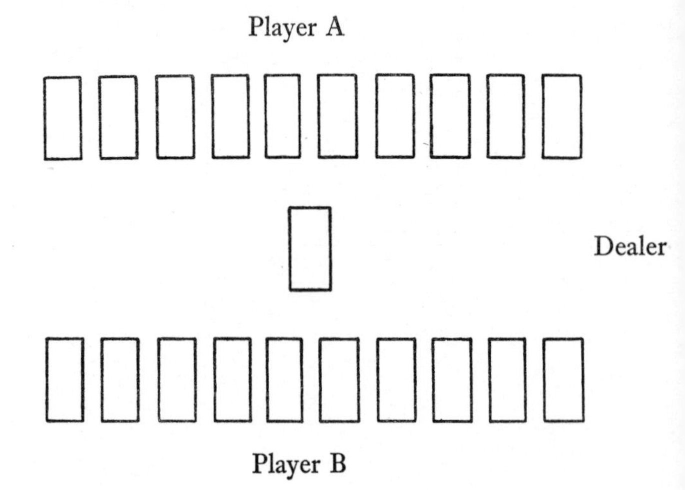

The dealer then places a card in the centre (for example, one bearing the number 15), and the first player to cover it with the card 9+6 scores a point. The first pupil to score 20 points wins the game.

(b) Lotto

A modified game of Lotto is very popular with children. Numbers of cards may be prepared for a game of Lotto, with the harder addition combinations. Each card, measuring 6 inches by 4, contains four rows of numbers with five in each row, the numbers being the answers to addition combinations. For example, one card may be:

16	11	18	13	15
8	16	13	11	5
17	6	14	12	7
16	12	13	9	17

Number combinations
8+8, 3+8, 9+9, 7+6, 8+7 etc.

Although many cards have many answers in common, they are also slightly different from each other in the actual numbers on them. The teacher then calls out a combination, *e.g.* 7+6. If they have the answer on their card the children cover it with a counter. The teacher may follow this with 10+0; the above sample card does not contain this.

(c) Cobbler Game

In this game a number of pupils are each given ten cards of a particular process. For example, pupils may be given the first ten facts in the list of division combinations (Set 10 in *Practice in Basic Arithmetic*, Book One). These are placed in a pile in front of them. One pupil is chosen as Cobbler. At a given command pupils select any four cards from their own piles and hide them in their hands. The Cobbler then says the following rhyme.

Nickety Nock, Nick Nock Noo,
How many buttons on my shoe ?
Maybe one, maybe two,
But I think 9 will do.

All pupils who hold in their hands cards the answer to which is 9 (or whichever number from 0 to 12 that the Cobbler may have called), give them to the Cobbler. Pupils pick up cards from their own piles to replace those given to the Cobbler. The game goes on until a pupil gets rid of all his cards, when he takes the Cobbler's place. When the Cobbler is changed, a new set of ten cards is given to each pupil.

(*d*) *Multiplication and Division Cards*

After pupils have made up their own multiplication and division tables from counters, cards can be prepared for practice. Suppose the 8 times table requires practice, then A and B cards, 6 inches by 4, are prepared as follows:

A CARD

9	2	8	3	9	7	6	4	0
3	2	12	0	9	8	9	10	1
11	9	8	7	6	12	9	8	7
6	5	12	4	11	9	8	10	4
6	3	2	1	8	9	6	7	12

B CARD

1	2	3	4	5	6	7	8	9	10	11	12
8	8	8	8	8	8	8	8	8	8	8	8
8	16	24	32	40	48	56	64	72	80	88	96

72	16	64	24	72	56	48	32	0
24	16	96	0	72	64	72	80	8
88	72	64	56	48	96	72	64	56
48	40	96	32	88	72	64	80	32
48	24	16	8	64	72	48	56	96

The children then work in pairs, those on the left of the seat being designated A, those on the right of the seat B. Pupil A takes card A and goes as quickly as possible through the process of multiplying by 8 the units on the card. Pupil B has card B which shows the answers and a check table at the top. Cards are then exchanged.

(*e*) *Jig-Saw Cards*

A modification of multiplication cards greatly enjoyed by normal as well as backward pupils are jig-saw cards. These are cards about 12 inches by 8 made of semi-stiff cardboard, and they are prepared as follows. Both cards are ruled with clear black lines into a number of irregularly shaped figures, one card being a replica of the other, but care being taken to see that no two figures on the same card are alike in shape. One card is first ruled and then pricked through on to the other card to ensure that the shapes on both are identical. On card B the elements of the table are written in varied order, one on each of the figures, while the correct product is written on the corresponding figure on the other card (card A).

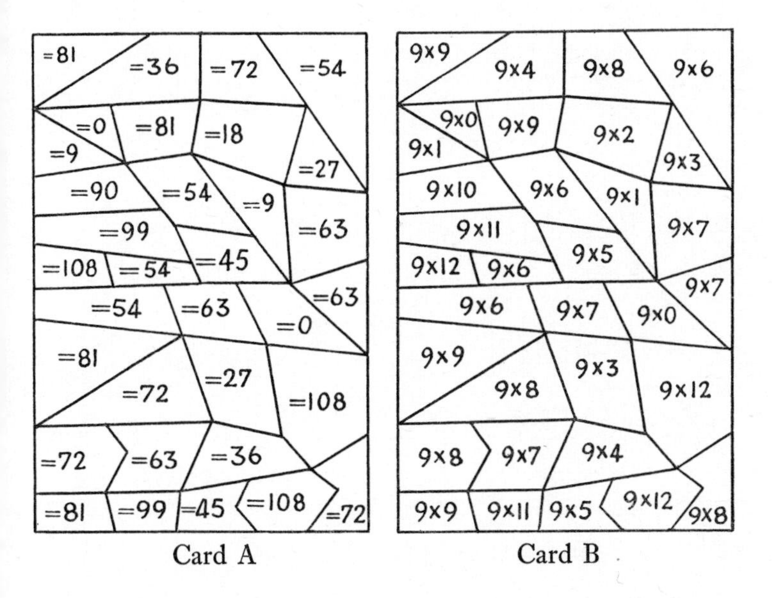

Card A Card B

Card A, complete with the products, is then cut up into shaped pieces. The pupil takes these pieces, on which the products are written, and places them in their correct positions on card B. It is not possible for him to make an error because each piece has only one position on card B, so that testing as well as teaching takes place. When card B is full the pupil simply lifts off the small pieces, repeating the multiplication fact, as he does so, to his partner or teacher. Speed tests and records of achievement from day to day can be kept for all such material.

A useful modification of the jig-saw arithmetic cards is that in which the base card (card B) has no lines on it, but merely the numbers. Pupils are thus forced to put each irregularly shaped card over the correct number without guidance from lines. At the same time the fact that all the pieces of cardboard should fit together like a jig-saw puzzle provides an automatic check.

(*f*) *Number Charts*

Another useful device for backward pupils is the number chart for variation in the four processes. The chart is compiled as follows:

1	2	3	4	5	6	7	8	9	10
11	12	13	14	15	16	17	18	19	20
21	22	23	24	25	26	27	28	29	30
31	32	33	34	35	36	37	38	39	40
41	42	43	44	45	46	47	48	49	50
51	52	53	54	55	56	57	58	59	60
61	62	63	64	65	66	67	68	69	70
71	72	73	74	75	76	77	78	79	80
81	82	83	84	85	86	87	88	89	90
91	92	93	94	95	96	97	98	99	100

Apart from the value of this chart for counting with very backward children all kinds of number facts with useful higher decade additions can be taught and tested from such a chart by taking rows of figures in different ways and different positions.

For example, each of the numbers 1 to 9 can be in turn added to all other numbers, thus:

11+5; 21+5; 31+5; 41+5; etc.
or 13+9; 23+9; 33+9; 43+9; etc.

and in this way much practice on higher decade addition is given.

Two further forms of very useful number charts are those constructed for practice with basic addition and subtraction facts.

CHART FOR EARLY ADDITION FACTS

	0	**1**	**2**	**3**	**4**	**5**	**6**	**7**	**8**	**9**	**10**
0	0	1	2	3	4	5	6	7	8	9	10
1	1	2	3	4	5	6	7	8	9	10	
2	2	3	4	5	6	7	8	9	10		
3	3	4	5	6	7	8	9	10			
4	4	5	6	7	8	9	10				
5	5	6	7	8	9	10					
6	6	7	8	9	10						
7	7	8	9	10							
8	8	9	10								
9	9	10									
10	10										

Children can be shown how to use the chart for practice in all number facts up to 10, including '0' combinations, by moving along the lines:

0+0=0, 0+1=1, 0+2=2, 0+3=3 etc.
1+0=1, 1+1=2, 1+2=3, 1+3=4 etc.
2+0=2, 2+1=3, 2+2=4, 2+3=5 etc.

The chart can be used by pairs of children, one asking the question and the other giving the answer, which may be checked from the chart.

SUBTRACTION CHART FOR COMBINATIONS UP TO 10

	1	**2**	**3**	**4**	**5**	**6**	**7**	**8**	**9**	**10**
0	1	2	3	4	5	6	7	8	9	10
1	0	1	2	3	4	5	6	7	8	9
2		0	1	2	3	4	5	6	7	8
3			0	1	2	3	4	5	6	7
4				0	1	2	3	4	5	6
5					0	1	2	3	4	5
6						0	1	2	3	4
7							0	1	2	3
8								0	1	2
9									0	1
10										0

Children can be shown how to use this chart for practice in subtraction, including ' 0 ' combinations, by moving along the lines:

0 from 1 is 1, 0 from 2 is 2, 0 from 3 is 3 etc.
1 from 1 is 0, 1 from 2 is 1, 1 from 3 is 2 etc.

Pupils not only enjoy learning their number facts by these devices through the interest and activity evoked but they learn them much more effectively.

Supplementary to card and chart practice, and as a midway step between concrete aids and abstract number work, the pupils should be given plenty of simple mental arithmetic in which the number facts are applied to everyday situations. All kinds of interesting material involving the various number combinations can be used for this work. The more stimulating the talk about the material or the situations the more vivid is the imagery aroused and the more interested are the pupils, so that they do their arithmetic without realising it is an arithmetic lesson. For example, a variety of number facts can be worked through in connection with numerous topics such as

(*a*) Birds sitting on telephone wires—changing positions to give different combinations.

(*b*) Clusters of cherries on a tree—picking them, giving some away, etc.

(*c*) Windows in a house, panes of glass in each window, etc.

(*d*) Milk bottles in a tray, delivery, rearranging, etc.

(*e*) Rose bushes in a garden, roses on the bushes, picking them, arranging them in vases, etc.

Everyday Applications of the Basic Number Facts

While provision for carefully distributed practice on the basic number combinations, supplemented by number activities such as those referred to above, can achieve a great deal in improving the arithmetic attainments of pupils, yet there is the need to provide activities in which the mechanical material is used in everyday situations. The more we can arrange for wider application of numbers to everyday activities, the more likely are we to increase a pupil's liking for arithmetic.

An effective use of experience units and projects can do much to change pupils' attitudes towards arithmetic, for such activities enable them to see that arithmetic can be meaningful, that it can be interesting and that it is useful. Because the arithmetic of a project is connected with the realistic needs of children, it is often pursued with much greater intellectual strength and purpose than if it had merely been an artificial classroom exercise.

The ideal remedial teaching programme combines carefully

prepared practice, which provides success and hence increases self-confidence, with opportunities for use of the material in everyday situations. In order to give adequate application of the number combinations outlined in the foregoing sections, all teachers should make some provision for activities such as those listed below.

1. *The Fruit Stall.* The classroom fruit stall can provide much useful everyday arithmetic. The project is made more interesting if children are allowed to make imitation fruits from papier mâché during their craft lessons. These are left to dry and painted in colours, and the preparation is completed by the printing of price tags for them. Fruits are then assembled, and children take turns at selling and buying.

2. *The Class Shop* should be a permanent part of the arithmetic syllabus. Children bring to school dummy or empty packets of foods and, from these, simply priced items are selected and then arranged with price tags on shelves to form a shop. Again, children take turns as shopkeeper and customers and thus get practice with many basic number combinations.

Both the fruit stall and the shop can be used at set times during the arithmetic lesson or for remedial sessions with particular groups of children.

3. *Cards for Special Occasions.* The making and purchase of birthday cards, Mother's Day cards, Christmas cards, etc. which are priced at 2d., 2½d., 3d., 3½d., 4d. etc. also provide experiences and material that can be used to advantage for consolidating pupils' knowledge of number combinations.

4. *A Model Post Office*, together with a model pillarbox, can be built up during handicraft lessons and then associated with both English and arithmetic activities. Children may be allowed to write letters and send small parcels though the 'post', and the transactions connected with the posting of these can take place at the model post office. In fact, this project can be an extremely useful means of informing children on post office business, particularly the purchase of stamps, the posting of parcels, the registering of letters, and the sending of telegrams. The teacher can extend the arithmetic of the post office project

by compiling numbers of simple problems based on the business of the post office and involving number combination practice.

5. *A Fair or Bazaar* can also form an excellent centre for practice of number combinations. Here the opportunity class or the special remedial group bring along objects which are sold to swell the funds for a class outing, the purchase of an object for the room, a donation to a social service fund, etc. Sometimes the material for the fair can be of the eatable kind. Pupils take turns as shop assistants and customers and gain practice in realistic situations.

6. *Necklaces, Bangles, etc.* Groups of very backward children can be encouraged to make necklaces, bangles and so on of small beads and shells of different colours and shapes, which are arranged according to different patterns. A certain amount of addition and subtraction can centre around the numbers of beads of different colours.

7. *Exercises on the Calendar* which relate to days, weeks, months, birthdays, to working out problems connected with school and home events, again provide situations with a maximum of motivation in terms of the arithmetic involved.

8. *Clock Face and Times.* The use of a clock face in number work is well known, but the interest that can be aroused in this activity will be enhanced if it is associated with routine times in the home and in the school, so that children have then to make calculations in regard to real events, such as how long they have to spend in school in the morning, how long it is from recess to lunch time, how long it takes them to come to school, and so forth.

9. *Bus and Tram Fares.* Information can be gathered from the class relating to the costs of journeys made, and much useful arithmetic can develop from the data supplied by the pupils.

10. *Shopping Lists.* Children should be encouraged to bring to school shopping lists that they use in connection with errands for their parents. One school I know replaces a good deal of its arithmetic for a month each year by the material provided by pupils themselves. A certain amount of selection is some-

times required beforehand by the teacher, but the use of real shopping lists certainly stimulates the interest in simple money transactions.

11. *Height and Weight Records.* Children are each given a card on which to record their height and their weight. Once a month the height and weight of each child is measured by the children, working in groups of six. Entries are made on the cards in inches and pounds and these are checked.

	My Weight	*My Height*
February	62 pounds	52 inches
March	62 pounds	53 inches
April	$62\frac{1}{2}$ pounds	$53\frac{1}{2}$ inches

Additional examples of this kind are provided in most modern textbooks on the teaching of arithmetic.

Summary

Thus the very backward pupils in this first group pass through four stages of remedial work. They are given

(*a*) opportunities to work with concrete materials to consolidate their number concepts, and in this stage they build up their own lists of basic number facts in addition and subtraction and their own multiplication and division tables with their boxes of counters;

(*b*) additional work on number combinations working from books with pictorial representations of concrete objects;

(*c*) distributed written drill on the basic number combinations from Book One of *Practice in Basic Arithmetic*, and individual and group games with cards or other material;

(*d*) distributed written drill on the higher decade extensions of the basic number combinations from Book Two of *Practice in Basic Arithmetic.*

When the pupil has made a certain amount of progress in this basic work he should be re-tested with Diagnostic Tests 1 to 4 to measure the amount of gain made. If there has been real consolidation of the basic work, a start can be made with simple graded examples in the four rules, as provided in Book Three of *Practice in Basic Arithmetic*.

In this and the next chapter I have concentrated—owing to confines of space—on those aspects of remedial work which deal principally with developing understanding and facility in the basic number combinations and their derivatives.[1] Naturally the entire arithmetic programme for children who are failing in arithmetic should also include adequate supplementary work in developing an understanding of the use of number as applied to money and common weights and measures.

[1] For some excellent suggestions on practical work, games and projects suited to a remedial teaching programme, see *Let's Play with Numbers*, by M. L. Wauchope (Whitcombe and Tombs).

CHAPTER IX

REMEDIAL TEACHING IN ARITHMETIC (FURTHER STAGES)

Group 2. Accuracy but very Slow Speed in Basic Number Work

In so far as the backward pupils in this group can make correct responses to the basic number combinations and their extensions if given sufficient time, it is an indication that they have some understanding at least of number concepts. But their extreme slowness is also an indication that (*a*) they require additional learning through the use of concrete material and real experiences and (*b*) they need practice with the basic number combinations and extensions.[1] With the children in this group there is not the need, I think, to take them systematically through the first two steps as outlined for those backward arithmeticians in Group 1. At the same time *it is essential that initially these children should be allowed to work through their addition and subtraction combinations with counters* before carrying out written drill with such material. There is research evidence to show that children who learn number combinations with understanding through the use of concrete material are quicker in their later responses than those who learn just by drill.[2] We have also found that these children improve rapidly when given a chance to consolidate their number facts through games (see Chapter VIII). Some have never experienced the fun and interest of a play approach; for them arithmetic has always been a kind of mechanical grind with numbers, never a game of skill with its stimulating competitive element.

Still others in this very slow-working group are slow because

[1] As set out in *Practice in Basic Arithmetic*, Books One and Two

[2] See for example Comparison of Individual-Concrete Methods and Class Methods in Teaching Arithmetic, by M. D. K. Morfitt, *Brit. J. Educ. Psych.*, June 1937.

they have not seen the purpose of it all. The arithmetic they do has not been connected with real-life situations and has not really meant anything to them. They have looked upon numbers as something connected only with school and have been unaware of the scores of little sums that come into their lives each day. One junior school solved this by encouraging children to report to their teachers actual shopping commissions they had done for their mothers and examples of any other simple arithmetic they, or members of their family, had used during the week. From the quite wide collection of examples received the classes, on certain days of the week, made up their own sums with greatly increased enjoyment and purpose in the arithmetic lessons.

Pupils in this group benefit greatly from doing numerous examples involving number combinations all centring round a topic or a practical exercise. Thus one may have a shop with articles for sale, the prices of which require the addition of 3 pennies and 6 pennies, of 4 pennies and 7 pennies, etc. Or one may give pupils line-drawing exercises to do on large sheets of paper:

Rule a line 5 inches long. Make it 8 inches longer. How long is it now?

Rule a line 10 inches long. Cut off 6 inches. How many inches are left?

Rule a line 15 inches long and another 7 inches long. How much longer is one than the other?

Improving Multiplication and Division

Sometimes in this group one finds pupils who are very slow because they do not understand what is meant by the processes of multiplication and division. They need activities with concrete materials that make manifest the relationships underlying multiplication and division processes.

This experience may proceed at first by dividing objects into groups (see pp. 141-42) and allowing pupils to form their own multiplication and division tables. Or it may proceed in a slightly modified way by enabling pupils to work gradually from discovery of the number facts about a small group of

objects to those about a large group of objects. Thus pupil
are given six counters. They indicate that this represents

six ones
three twos
two threes.

They then write

6 groups of 1 counter are 6 counters.
6 groups of 1 are 6.
$6 \times 1 = 6$.

Then they do likewise with the other information.

The teacher asks, 'What can you divide 2 into, 4 into, 5 into?
Then they discover the relationships of 8, 12, 15, 16, 18, 20
21, 24, etc. From this experience they can then write thei
one times and two times multiplication tables and correspondin
division tables. By extending their discovery of numbe
relationships to 36 and 48 counters they can build up thei
3 and 4 times multiplication and associated division tables.

Distributed drill should follow this understanding gaine
through the concrete.

The case of John M., age 12½ years, I.Q. 97-105 (Terma
Merrill), illustrates difficulties common to pupils in Group 2
In the diagnosis of his backwardness John was given th
following tests with these results:

Diagnostic Arithmetic Tests

Test	*Arithmetic Age*	*Extent Retarded*
1 (+ Facts)	12·4	—
2 (– Facts)	10·8	1 yr, 10 mths
3 (× Facts)	9·5	3 yrs, 1 mth
4 (÷ Facts)	9·7	2 yrs, 11 mths
5 (Misc. Facts)	9·3	3 yrs, 3 mths
6 (Graded +)	11·11	7 mths
7 (Graded –)	8·8	3 yrs, 10 mths
8A (Graded ×)	9·8	2 yrs, 10 mths
8B (Graded ×)	9·5	3 yrs, 1 mth
9 (Graded ÷)	9·6	3 yrs

	Arithmetic Age	*Re-test after six months*	*Gain*
Mechanical Arithmetic Test A	10·4	11·4	1 yr
Problem Arithmetic Test A	10·3	11·4	1 yr, 1 mth

John showed in his initial tests slowness and some inaccuracy with the number combinations and their extensions. He was up to normal standard in addition but 2 years, 3 years and 4 years behind in his basic subtraction, multiplication and division facts respectively. In his subtraction facts applied to subtraction sums (as in Test 7) his score indicated a leeway of 4 years.

He made such subtraction errors as

$15-6=10 \qquad 13-5=6 \qquad 12-5=6$
$14-9=6 \qquad 13-9=5 \qquad 13-6=8;$

multiplication errors as

$7\times9=32 \qquad 1\times0=1 \qquad 2\times3=5$
$3\times2=5$ (a peculiarly persistent error)
$6\times9=72 \qquad 9\times3=21 \qquad 7\times8=54;$

division errors as

$6\div2=2 \qquad 9\div1=8 \qquad 32\div4=7 \qquad 2\div1=1$
$5\div5=0 \qquad 4\div4=0 \qquad 35\div7=8 \qquad 42\div7=7$
$64\div8=9 \qquad 0\div5=5 \qquad 5\div5=0 \qquad 7\div7=0.$

He also showed in Test 5, which assesses ability in difficult number facts in the four rules in jumbled order, that he could not keep his mind on the meaning of the signs as they changed; thus he made errors like

$63\div9=55$
$64\div8=56$ (obviously subtracting)
$5+7=35$ (multiplying).

These errors in the basic number combinations were scattered throughout his work in the four processes (Tests 6, 7, 8A, 8B, 9). John's weakness in his fundamental arithmetic seemed to be caused partly by emotional factors due to insecurity and loss of confidence and partly by intermittent absences which undermined his accuracy in basic arithmetic work. His father was an alcoholic who drank himself to death over a five-year period, in which the tension and difficulties of the home, emotional and physical, were extremely great. John began to fail in his arithmetic as a result of this tension, and his continued failure then caused him to lose confidence. His home difficulties and school failure were connected with a complete change in his attitude towards his friends, his teachers and towards his life problems. As a result of the tension he shrank from friends and revealed most obvious feelings of inferiority. A period of therapeutic help to him and to his mother, and actual economic assistance to her, has resulted in marked improvement in the attitudes of both.

For John, this psychological help was linked with planned remedial teaching. He worked with interest through the graded remedial material in Books One and Two of *Practice in Basic Arithmetic*. He deserved the constant praise given, and derived satisfaction and stimulation from the obvious progress he made in the sets of graded combinations, as evidenced by his scores on successive occasions.

At the end of five months John was given a re-test with the diagnostic tests. His scores were as follows:

Test	*Re-test after* 5 *months*	*Gain*
1 (+ Facts)	12·8	4 mths
2 (− Facts)	11·9	1 yr, 1 mth
3 (× Facts)	11·9	2 yrs, 4 mths
4 (÷ Facts)	12·4	2 yrs, 9 mths
7 (Graded −)	11·4	2 yrs, 8 mths
8A (Graded ×)	11·4	1 yr, 8 mths
8B (Graded ×)	11·4	1 yr, 9 mths
9 (Graded ÷)	11·6	2 yrs

Furthermore, this progress was evidenced in his improvement in ordinary classwork.

GROUP 3. FAIR ACCURACY ACCOMPANIED BY INDIVIDUAL ERRORS

In this group are *pupils who show persistent individual errors of a particular kind.* Although there is great variety in the pattern of errors, many of them are to be found among

(*a*) the '0' combinations;[1] *e.g.* $6+0$, $7-0$, 8×0, $8\div0$;

(*b*) like figure combinations in subtraction; *e.g.* $5-5$;

(*c*) those specially difficult combinations[2] in each of the four rules.

These individual errors are best eliminated by a combination of practice, both in basic number facts and in applied form. Pupils benefit from working selected pages in Books One and Two of *Practice in Basic Arithmetic.* A rational approach which emphasises the relationships of the particular combination in which the pupil is making errors is often of value.

Thus with a pupil making errors in zero combinations we might say: 'Here are eight 0s: 0, 0, 0, 0, 0, 0, 0, 0. How much do they add up to? What is the product of nine 0s, of ten 0s? How much is six 0s? Take away four 0s.'

This approach helps such children to break bad number habits but, as we all know, habits are established by continuous responses of the same kind, setting up a particular nerve trace or pathway and we need just as continuously to respond in the correct way to eliminate the old and establish the new. Hence rational explanation can only help; a certain amount of repetitive practice is essential.

GROUP 4. INSUFFICIENT UNDERSTANDING OF THE FOUR PROCESSES

These are pupils who have developed an effective working accuracy in the fundamental number combinations and their

[1] For a short discussion on zero difficulties of children see Chapter X of *The Case Against Arithmetic*, by E. M. Renwick (Simpkin Marshall).

[2] Test 5, *Diagnostic Arithmetic Tests*, contains a collection of these. The combinations that most frequently cause errors are shown in *Practice in Basic Arithmetic, Teacher's Handbook.*

extensions but who break down at a particular point in the process of subtraction or division or multiplication (addition is usually mastered). They are on the whole the easiest group to help. The fact that they have not yet mastered the idea of 'borrowing' in subtraction, or of trial divisors in long division, or of compound multiplication is not very serious, provided there is facility with the basic number combinations, which in fact constitute the major part of the calculation. What these pupils obviously need is remedial work with sets of examples on each step of difficulty in the process. Thus, as a result of repeated absences, Tim, aged 14, had not had sufficient continuous instruction really to grasp the idea of 'borrowing' in subtraction.

In his results of Diagnostic Test 7 he did not get any example correct after line B. His attempt at line C (involving borrowing) was:

$$\begin{array}{rrrrrrrr} 71 & 62 & 46 & 84 & 54 & 22 & 58 & 46 \\ -2 & -4 & -7 & -6 & -39 & -17 & -19 & -27 \\ \hline 70 & 60 & 40 & 80 & 20 & 10 & 40 & 20 \\ \hline \end{array}$$

In his case he was given a few examples in which he had to add the difference to the subtrahend to get the minuend, as in

$$\begin{array}{rr} ? & ? \\ -8 & -7 \\ \hline 9 & 8 \\ \hline \end{array}$$

Then he was given examples such as

$$\begin{array}{rrrr} 10 & 10 & 20 & 30 \\ -1 & -2 & -3 & -4 \\ \hline & & & \\ \hline \end{array}$$

to give the idea of breaking into the next 10.

Following this, he did examples such as

$$\begin{array}{rrrrrrl} 11 & 21 & 31 & 41 & 51 & 61 & \text{etc.} \\ -2 & -2 & -2 & -2 & -2 & -2 & \\ \hline & & & & & & \\ \hline \end{array}$$

11	21	31	41	51	61 etc.
−3	−3	−3	−3	−3	−3
—	—	—	—	—	—

and these were continued with examples up to 100, with subtrahends of 4, 5, 6, 7, 8, 9. In a further set the minuends were increased from 11, 21, etc. to 12, 22, etc., to 13, 23, etc. and so on. Then he was given an example of the type 23−18 and asked to give a result by inspection and to state the principle employed in borrowing, using the method of decomposition. (Naturally, with children who have not mastered the process, the method of equal addition might easily be taught, but it is not so easy to demonstrate to pupils.)

He was then asked to work the examples in Sets Four, Five, Six and Seven in *Right from the Start Arithmetic*, Book I, pp. 66-69. These were followed by the puzzles on pp. 69 and 70.

Need for Grading of Examples in Remedial Work

The difficulties of all children of this group (Group 4) are revealed through Tests 6, 7, 8A, 8B, 9, 10 and 11. With children aged 9+ upwards these tests should always be worked without time limit, so that results from the entire tests, or as much as pupils are able to do, will reveal the points of weakness.

Thus Tim, aged 10½, gets every example correct in Test 8A up to line E (*d*) but fails thereafter because he does not know how to do compound multiplication.

The diagnostic tests set out the four processes in the following numbers of steps:

Test 6	Graded Addition	14 steps	(see pp. 92-4)
Test 7	Graded Subtraction	14 steps	(see pp. 96-8)
Test 8	Graded Multiplication	14 steps	(see pp. 100-2)
Test 9	Graded Division	11 steps	(see pp. 102-3)
Test 10	Long Division	9 steps	(see pp. 104-5)
Test 11	Long Division	6 steps	(see pp. 105-6)

Remedial material which exactly follows these various steps in each test, is given in Book Three of *Practice in Basic Arithmetic*. These sets of graded material are closely linked to the steps in each diagnostic test, and enable teachers to start children off with remedial work at the exact step in which weakness is revealed in the diagnostic test.

Remedial Material in Addition

Graded material covering the steps 1, 2, 3 and 4 of Diagnostic Test 6.

Book I, *Right from the Start Arithmetic*, pp. 10-11.

Additional practice material involving hundreds, tens and units without carrying is provided in Book Three of *Practice in Basic Arithmetic*.

Graded material covering steps 5-14 has been given in Book Three of *Practice in Basic Arithmetic* and has been divided into:

(*a*) examples in which the carrying figure is restricted to 1 in either tens or units column;

(*b*) examples in which the carrying figure is restricted to 2.

There are additional graded, miscellaneous examples in *Right from the Start Arithmetic*, Book I, pp. 61-62, with puzzles on pp. 63-64, and in Book II, pp. 12-15, with puzzles on p. 16.

Remedial Material in Subtraction

Graded material covering steps 1, 2, 3 and 4 of Diagnostic Test 7, *i.e.* examples without borrowing, are given in Book Three of *Practice in Basic Arithmetic*, and Sets One, Two, Three (pp. 65-66) in Book I *Right from the Start Arithmetic*.

Graded material covering steps 5-14 is given in Book Three of *Practice in Basic Arithmetic* and also in Sets Four, Five, Six, Seven, pp. 66-69 in Book I, *Right from the Start Arithmetic*, with puzzles on pp. 69-70.

Remedial Material in Multiplication

Graded material covering steps 1, 2, 3 (no carrying) in *Practice in Basic Arithmetic*, Book Three.

Graded material covering steps 5-14 in *Practice in Basic Arithmetic*, Book Three.

Right from the Start Arithmetic, Book I, Sets One, Two, Three, Four, Five, Six, Seven (pp. 72-75). Puzzles pp. 76-77.

Remedial Material in Division

Book Three of *Practice in Basic Arithmetic.*

Right from the Start Arithmetic, Book I. Division preparation with remedial work on tables, pp. 78-79, Sets One, Two, Three, Four, pp. 80-84. Puzzles pp. 84-85.

Improvement in Problems

The task of eliminating backwardness is difficult enough in mechanical arithmetic, but it is doubly so when we deal with problem-solving, progress in which is for most children a matter of constant practice with stereotyped examples, each characterised by its particular clues and catchwords. The difficulty arises from two sources: firstly, ability to solve problems is very closely related to level of general intelligence, hence dull pupils will almost invariably experience difficulty with problem arithmetic; secondly, this ability is dependent upon numerous other factors such as reading, memory and computational accuracy.

The essentials in problem-solving might be enumerated as follows:

1. intelligent reading of the problem;
2. technique of attack: analysis and arrangement of data;
3. seeing relationships between the data;
4. seeing an analogy with similar problems;
5. selecting and reproducing the process;
6. accurate computation;
7. approximate checking of the result.

The discerning teacher will see that in certain of these steps, namely 3, 4, 5, it will be difficult to bring about improvement, but in others improvement will take place if definite attention is given to the specific step. Thus, as problems contain both verbal and numerical materials which are read in somewhat different ways, noticeable improvement in problem-solving follows practice in problem-reading. Pupils should be trained to make a first reading to understand the principle involved, a second to appreciate the details of the numbers, and a third, attending to both principle and numbers. This procedure minimises premature generalisation, incorrect transcription of numbers and the loss of confidence experienced when large numbers are met with at the beginning of a problem.

Improvement in phases 3, 4 and 5 must be brought about by replacing reasoning power and novelty, as far as possible, by memory and imitation, *i.e.* by a careful division of problems into types, then a treatment of a variety of sub-types.

At times the pupil is handicapped in problem-solving because insufficient practice is devoted to easy one-step problems of an everyday nature that cover all combinations of addition, subtraction, multiplication and division. Junior pupils benefit from considerable practice in these simple problems, some examples of which follow:

Example 1. (Addition and subtraction.)

A boy is in school for 3 hours in the morning. Assembly takes 15 minutes, arithmetic 40 minutes, milk 5 minutes, playtime 15 minutes and the rest of the morning is taken up by a drawing lesson. How long is the drawing lesson?

Example 2. (Multiplication and addition.)

On Monday Mother took $2\frac{1}{2}$ pints of milk and on each of the other days, except Sunday, she took $1\frac{1}{2}$ pints. On Sunday she took 3 pints. How many pints did she take for the whole week?

Example 3. (Multiplication and subtraction.)

Last month the gas cost Mother 2s. 7d. a week, but this month it cost her only 1s. 11d. a week. How much more did it cost her last month? (4 weeks = one month.)

Example 4. (Multiplication and division.)

There are 5 apples to a pound. Mother has 6 pounds to last 3 days. How many apples should she use each day?

Example 5. (Subtraction and addition.)

Fresh butter is 1s. 4d. a pound and salt butter is 3d. a pound less. How much must I pay for a pound of salt and a pound of fresh butter?

Example 6. (Addition and division.)

Mother had 3s. 6d. in silver, 2d. in pennies, as well as 4d. in halfpennies. This was just enough to buy a joint of 4 pounds of beef. How much a pound was the beef?[1]

The teacher should remember that an inductive-deductive approach is the best for general problem-solving, but for particular types of problems taken one at a time the deductive seems superior.

Group 5. Less Able Pupils

For the fifth group of children, whose slowness and inaccuracy in arithmetic are largely due to their lower intelligence, there are four cardinal principles that have a bearing on remedial work:

(*a*) the extent of their work in arithmetic must be considerably reduced;

(*b*) the method of grading their work should follow that given in Books One, Two and Three of *Practice in Basic Arithmetic* and Book I of *Right from the Start Arithmetic;*

(*c*) there should be an even more intensive use of the concrete in teaching them arithmetic than has been urged in the above sections;

(*d*) their arithmetic should be applied to practical learning situations connected with shopping, gardening, domestic science, handicrafts, dressmaking, woodwork and metal working.

[1] See Book I of *Right from the Start Arithmetic* (Oliver and Boyd) for 160 of such problems which cover all possible combinations. The problems, which are suitable for normal pupils of 8 and 9 years of age and for backward ones of all ages, are graded, while those combinations most commonly used in everyday life receive additional emphasis.

It is essential that their arithmetic should consist of a carefully devised programme of learning through the concrete, with continuous application to real situations in the classroom (the shop, post office, etc.) and to the practical subjects in the curriculum. This is not the place to outline in detail all the steps of teaching arithmetic to children in special or opportunity classes,[1] *except to emphasise that the remedial measures discussed in the foregoing pages may be applied with particular value to the arithmetic of all slow-learning children.*

It is important, in regard to the function of arithmetic in the minds of dull children, that they should not be kept at mechanical exercises or practice drills, with the idea that their speed and accuracy must be improved before embarking on applied arithmetic. Their arithmetic should be taught mainly through the concrete, and applied to practical situations, but some consolidation of the fundamental number combinations should be undertaken each day by means of *Practice in Basic Arithmetic* Books One and Two. If pupils are helped to keep individual records of their progress in each set of examples, the daily practice takes on something of the spirit of a competition in which everyone is achieving a degree of success.

Conclusion

It will be apparent throughout this chapter that pupils requiring remedial help fall into two major groups: those who need concrete and practical experiences to facilitate their initial understanding and learning of the basic number material followed by systematic drill, and secondly those pupils who require basic drill allied to numerous practical applications of the fundamental number knowledge to produce working efficiency in them. The measures for both groups are, of course, overlapping, but reference to the main needs of each does throw up important remedial principles.

[1] Very useful information on steps in the development of number relationships through the use of concrete material is contained in *Arithmetic Kindergarten—Grade Three* (Board of Education of the City of New York, Curriculum Bulletin, No. 2).

Finally, it cannot be too strongly emphasised that *every* pupil backward in arithmetic must receive some measure of individual attention in his difficulties. He must feel that his failure, his confusion, and what is for many a child his only source of worry, are receiving the consideration of a person who can really help him and provide him with success. For many children, especially intelligent ones, backwardness in arithmetic may burrow quite deeply into their happiness in school, into their self-esteem and even into their physical health, for it is not uncommon to see at the Remedial Education Centre children who do not want to go to school because of their failure in arithmetic, or children whose sleep is disturbed by worry over arithmetic.

It is often through the first individual contacts between pupil and remedial teacher that the effects of failure begin to be dispersed, and it is through the child's belief in his helper that he applies himself to his remedial work. Strength of belief that he will be able to do arithmetic through his help—hence the vital value of early success and encouragement—is a deciding factor in determining whether he will make progress or not. Scientific diagnosis of difficulties and carefully planned remedial work are therefore only part of the treatment needed for success—the effect of the bond between teacher and pupil will often do as much to overcome disability as any other measure. With many children backward in arithmetic, particularly the rather sensitive highly intelligent ones, their disability is not due to lack of intelligence but to lack of confidence in their own powers to succeed in arithmetic.

The following arithmetic tests with their norms, answers and instructions are all contained in *Diagnostic and Attainment Testing* (Third Edition), by F. J. and F. E. Schonell (Oliver and Boyd).

Diagnostic Arithmetic Tests

Diagnostic Tests in Vulgar Fractions, Decimal Fractions and Percentages (by F. J. Schonell, J. Richardson and K. P. O'Connor)

Essential Mechanical Arithmetic Tests, Forms A and B

Essential Problem Arithmetic Tests, Forms A and B

APPENDIX I

AVERAGE SCORES AND EQUIVALENT ARITHMETIC AGES FOR *DIAGNOSTIC ARITHMETIC TESTS* 1-12 IN GIVEN TIMES

Test 1. Addition Combinations

Time—3 minutes

Score	Arith. Age		Score	Arith. Age		Score	Arith. Age	
	Yrs.	Mths.		Yrs.	Mths.		Yrs.	Mths.
25	7	0	51	9	1	76	11	1
27	7	1	52	9	2	77	11	2
28	7	2	53	9	3	78	11	4
29	7	3	54	9	3	79	11	5
30	7	4	55	9	4	80	11	6
31	7	5	56	9	5	81	11	7
32	7	6	57	9	6	82	11	8
33	7	7	58	9	7	83	11	8
34	7	8	59	9	8	84	11	10
35	7	9	60	9	9	85	12	0
36	7	10	61	9	10	86	12	4
37	7	11	62	9	11	87	12	6
38	8	1	63	10	0	88	12	8
39	8	2	64	10	0	89	12	10
40	8	3	65	10	1	90	13	0
41	8	4	66	10	2	91	13	2
42	8	5	67	10	3	92	13	4
43	8	6	68	10	4	93	13	6
44	8	7	69	10	5	94	13	10
45	8	8	70	10	6	95	14	2
46	8	9	71	10	7	96	14	6
47	8	9	72	10	8	97	14	9
48	8	10	73	10	10	98	15	0+
49	8	11	74	10	11	..	..	
50	9	0	75	11	0	..	..	

TEST 2. SUBTRACTION COMBINATIONS

Time—3½ minutes

Score	Arith. Age		Score	Arith. Age		Score	Arith. Age	
	Yrs.	Mths.		Yrs.	Mths.		Yrs.	Mths.
23	7	0	49	9	0	74	10	11
25	7	1	50	9	1	75	11	0
26	7	2	51	9	2	76	11	1
27	7	3	52	9	2	77	11	2
28	7	4	53	9	3	78	11	4
29	7	5	54	9	4	79	11	5
30	7	6	55	9	5	80	11	6
31	7	7	56	9	5	81	11	8
32	7	8	57	9	6	82	11	10
33	7	9	58	9	7	83	12	0
34	7	10	59	9	8	84	12	2
35	8	0	60	9	9	85	12	4
36	8	1	61	9	10	86	12	6
37	8	2	62	9	11	87	12	9
38	8	3	63	10	0	88	13	0
39	8	4	64	10	0	89	13	3
40	8	5	65	10	1	90	13	6
41	8	6	66	10	2	91	13	9
42	8	7	67	10	3	92	14	0
43	8	8	68	10	4	93	14	3
44	8	8	69	10	5	94	14	6
45	8	9	70	10	6	95	14	9
46	8	10	71	10	7	96	15	0+
47	8	11	72	10	8	..	..	
48	8	11	73	10	10	..	..	

TEST 3. MULTIPLICATION COMBINATIONS

Time—3 minutes

Score	Arith. Age		Score	Arith. Age		Score	Arith. Age	
	Yrs.	Mths.		Yrs.	Mths.		Yrs.	Mths.
16	7	0	41	9	3	66	11	2
17	7	1	42	9	4	67	11	3
18	7	2	43	9	5	68	11	4
19	7	4	44	9	6	69	11	5
20	7	5	45	9	7	70	11	6
21	7	6	46	9	8	71	11	8
22	7	7	47	9	9	72	11	9
23	7	8	48	9	9	73	11	11
24	7	10	49	9	10	74	12	0
25	7	11	50	9	11	75	12	2
26	8	0	51	10	0	76	12	3
27	8	1	52	10	1	77	12	5
28	8	2	53	10	2	78	12	6
29	8	4	54	10	3	79	12	8
30	8	5	55	10	3	80	12	10
31	8	6	56	10	4	81	13	0
32	8	7	57	10	5	82	13	2
33	8	8	58	10	6	83	13	4
34	8	9	59	10	7	84	13	6
35	8	10	60	10	8	85	13	10
36	8	11	61	10	9	86	14	2
37	9	0	62	10	10	87	14	6
38	9	0	63	10	11	88	14	9
39	9	1	64	11	0	89	15	0+
40	9	2	65	11	1	..	..	

TEST 4. DIVISION COMBINATIONS

Time—3 minutes

Score	Arith. Age		Score	Arith. Age		Score	Arith. Age	
	Yrs.	Mths.		Yrs.	Mths.		Yrs.	Mths.
8	7	0	35	9	7	62	11	4
9	7	1	36	9	8	63	11	5
10	7	2	37	9	8	64	11	6
11	7	4	38	9	9	65	11	7
12	7	5	39	9	10	66	11	8
13	7	6	40	9	11	67	11	10
14	7	8	41	9	11	68	11	11
15	7	9	42	10	0	69	12	0
16	7	11	43	10	1	70	12	1
17	8	0	44	10	2	71	12	2
18	8	2	45	10	2	72	12	4
19	8	3	46	10	3	73	12	5
20	8	5	47	10	4	74	12	6
21	8	6	48	10	5	75	12	8
22	8	7	49	10	5	76	12	10
23	8	8	50	10	6	77	13	0
24	8	9	51	10	7	78	13	2
25	8	10	52	10	8	79	13	4
26	8	11	53	10	9	80	13	6
27	9	0	54	10	9	81	13	9
28	9	0	55	10	10	82	14	0
29	9	1	56	10	11	83	14	3
30	9	2	57	11	0	84	14	6
31	9	3	58	11	1	85	14	9
32	9	4	59	11	2	86	15	0+
33	9	5	60	11	3	..	..	
34	9	6	61	11	3	..	..	

TEST 5. MISCELLANEOUS COMBINATIONS

Time—5 minutes

Score	Arith. Age		Score	Arith. Age		Score	Arith. Age	
	Yrs.	Mths.		Yrs.	Mths.		Yrs.	Mths.
4	7	0	32	9	8	59	11	9
6	7	2	33	9	9	60	11	10
7	7	4	34	9	10	61	11	11
8	7	6	35	9	11	62	12	0
9	7	8	36	10	0	63	12	1
10	7	9	37	10	1	64	12	2
11	7	11	38	10	2	65	12	3
12	8	0	39	10	3	66	12	4
13	8	2	40	10	4	67	12	5
14	8	3	41	10	5	68	12	6
15	8	5	42	10	6	69	12	8
16	8	6	43	10	7	70	12	9
17	8	7	44	10	8	71	12	11
18	8	8	45	10	9	72	13	0
19	8	8	46	10	9	73	13	2
20	8	9	47	10	10	74	13	3
21	8	10	48	10	11	75	13	5
22	8	11	49	11	0	76	13	6
23	9	0	50	11	1	77	13	8
24	9	2	51	11	2	78	13	11
25	9	2	52	11	3	79	14	1
26	9	3	53	11	3	80	14	4
27	9	3	54	11	4	81	14	6
28	9	4	55	11	5	82	14	9
29	9	5	56	11	6	83	15	0+
30	9	6	57	11	7	..	..	
31	9	7	58	11	8	..	..	

TEST 6. GRADED ADDITION

Time—6 minutes

Score	Arith. Age		Score	Arith. Age		Score	Arith. Age	
	Yrs.	Mths.		Yrs.	Mths.		Yrs.	Mths.
11	7	0	26	8	10	41	10	6
12	7	2	27	8	11	42	10	9
13	7	3	28	9	1	43	10	11
14	7	4	29	9	2	44	11	1
15	7	6	30	9	3	45	11	4
16	7	8	31	9	5	46	11	6
17	7	9	32	9	6	47	11	9
18	7	10	33	9	7	48	12	0
19	7	11	34	9	9	49	12	3
20	8	2	35	9	10	50	12	6
21	8	3	36	9	11	51	13	0
22	8	5	37	10	1	52	13	6
23	8	6	38	10	2	53	14	0
24	8	7	39	10	3	54	14	6
25	8	9	40	10	5	55	15	0

TEST 7. GRADED SUBTRACTION

Time—6 minutes

Score	Arith. Age		Score	Arith. Age		Score	Arith. Age	
	Yrs.	Mths.		Yrs.	Mths.		Yrs.	Mths.
5	7	0	22	9	6	39	11	9
6	7	2	23	9	7	40	12	0
7	7	4	24	9	8	41	12	3
8	7	6	25	9	9	42	12	6
9	7	8	26	9	11	43	12	9
10	7	9	27	10	1	44	13	0
11	7	11	28	10	2	45	13	3
12	8	1	29	10	3	46	13	6
13	8	2	30	10	5	47	13	8
14	8	4	31	10	6	48	13	10
15	8	6	32	10	8	49	14	0
16	8	8	33	10	9	50	14	2
17	8	9	34	10	11	51	14	4
18	8	11	35	11	1	52	14	6
19	9	1	36	11	2	53	14	8
20	9	2	37	11	4	54	14	10
21	9	4	38	11	6	55	15	0

TEST 8A. GRADED MULTIPLICATION

Time—7 minutes

Score	Arith. Age		Score	Arith. Age		Score	Arith. Age	
	Yrs.	Mths.		Yrs.	Mths.		Yrs.	Mths.
5	7	0	18	9	4	31	11	11
6	7	3	19	9	6	32	12	1
7	7	6	20	9	8	33	12	4
8	7	8	21	9	11	34	12	6
9	7	11	22	10	1	35	12	9
10	8	1	23	10	4	36	13	0
11	8	4	24	10	6	37	13	3
12	8	6	25	10	8	38	13	6
13	8	8	26	10	11	39	14	0
14	8	9	27	11	1	40	14	6
15	8	11	28	11	4	41	15	0
16	9	1	29	11	6	..	..	
17	9	2	30	11	8	..	..	

TEST 8B. GRADED MULTIPLICATION

Time—7 minutes

Score	Arith. Age		Score	Arith. Age	
	Yrs.	Mths.		Yrs.	Mths.
1	9	0	7	11	6
2	9	6	8	12	0
3	9	10	9	12	6
4	10	2	10 {	13	6
5	10	6		14	6
6	11	0	..	..	

TEST 9. GRADED DIVISION

Time—5 minutes

Score	Arith. Age		Score	Arith. Age		Score	Arith. Age	
	Yrs.	Mths.		Yrs.	Mths.		Yrs.	Mths.
2	7	0	16	9	4	30	11	6
3	7	2	17	9	6	31	11	8
4	7	4	18	9	8	32	11	11
5	7	6	19	9	9	33	12	1
6	7	8	20	9	11	34	12	4
7	7	10	21	10	1	35	12	6
8	8	0	22	10	3	36	12	10
9	8	2	23	10	4	37	13	2
10	8	4	24	10	6	38	13	6
11	8	6	25	10	8	39	13	10
12	8	8	26	10	10	40	14	2
13	8	10	27	11	0	41	14	6
14	9	0	28	11	2	42	15	0
15	9	2	29	11	4	..	..	

TEST 10. GRADED LONG DIVISION (EASY STEPS)

Time—9 minutes

Score	Arith. Age		Score	Arith. Age		Score	Arith. Age	
	Yrs.	Mths.		Yrs.	Mths.		Yrs.	Mths.
7	9	0	17	10	5	27	12	6
8	9	2	18	10	7	28	12	10
9	9	4	19	10	9	29	13	2
10	9	6	20	10	11	30	13	6
11	9	8	21	11	1	31	13	10
12	9	9	22	11	4	32	14	2
13	9	11	23	11	6	33	14	6
14	10	0	24	11	9	34	14	10
15	10	2	25	12	0	..	..	
16	10	3	26	12	3	..	..	

Test 11. Graded Long Division (harder steps)

Time—15 *minutes*

Score	Arith. Age		Score	Arith. Age		Score	Arith. Age	
	Yrs.	Mths.		Yrs.	Mths.		Yrs.	Mths.
1	9	0	8	10	9	15	12	10
2	9	6	9	11	0	16	13	0
3	9	8	10	11	3	17	13	6
4	9	11	11	11	6	18	14	0
5	10	1	12	11	10	19	14	6
6	10	4	13	12	2	20	15	0
7	10	6	14	12	6	..	..	

Test 12. Graded Mental Arithmetic

Time—10 *minutes*

Score	Arith. Age		Score	Arith. Age		Score	Arith. Age	
	Yrs.	Mths.		Yrs.	Mths.		Yrs.	Mths.
3	7	0	15	9	2	27	11	9
4	7	2	16	9	5	28	12	0
5	7	4	17	9	7	29	12	3
6	7	6	18	9	10	30	12	6
7	7	8	19	10	0	31	12	9
8	7	10	20	10	2	32	13	0
9	8	0	21	10	5	33	13	6
10	8	2	22	10	7	34	14	0
11	8	5	23	10	10	35	..	
12	8	7	24	11	0	36	..	
13	8	10	25	11	3	..	..	
14	9	0	26	11	6	..	..	

APPENDIX II

ANSWERS TO THE SCHONELL *DIAGNOSTIC ARITHMETIC TESTS* 1-12

Answers to the items in the twelve tests are set out below. When pupils are correcting their own results teachers should remember to call answers across the pages, that is in the order in which the sums have been worked.

Test 1. Addition

100 Basic Addition Facts

	(*a*)	(*b*)	(*c*)	(*d*)	(*e*)
A.	2	0	4	3	4
B.	2	4	6	10	5
C.	7	4	8	8	7
D.	8	9	6	5	14
E.	7	5	5	2	12
F.	7	16	11	10	9
G.	11	10	18	3	7
H.	1	6	8	6	4
I.	10	10	10	9	8
J.	11	6	9	3	3
K.	5	6	9	9	9
L.	1	8	9	8	7
M.	5	7	7	8	8
N.	9	12	6	10	12
O.	9	10	11	11	10
P.	11	11	12	13	12
Q.	13	11	17	12	13
R.	12	14	13	14	15
S.	14	15	15	17	16
T.	14	15	13	13	16

Test 2. Subtraction

100 Basic Subtraction Facts

	(*a*)	(*b*)	(*c*)	(*d*)	(*e*)
A.	1	0	2	1	0
B.	2	0	4	0	7
C.	0	1	2	1	1
D.	3	5	8	0	1
E.	0	6	3	0	3
F.	4	4	0	1	2
G.	1	9	2	6	2
H.	4	3	6	6	5
I.	3	9	3	5	8
J.	6	4	4	0	1
K.	6	2	3	2	8
L.	7	5	5	7	3
M.	9	4	4	7	3
N.	5	2	6	1	3
O.	7	8	4	8	2
P.	5	7	7	7	9
Q.	8	7	8	5	9
R.	6	6	5	9	8
S.	8	9	9	7	6
T.	8	9	5	4	9

Test 3. Multiplication

100 Basic Multiplication Facts

	(*a*)	(*b*)	(*c*)	(*d*)	(*e*)
A.	3	4	7	2	4
B.	5	10	6	16	5
C.	4	6	8	6	18
D.	20	14	16	6	10
E.	3	9	9	15	12
F.	2	12	12	25	24
G.	18	36	8	20	18
H.	30	8	12	15	27
I.	32	30	40	35	24
J.	45	1	48	54	42
K.	36	21	28	24	7
L.	14	18	16	9	0
M.	8	24	21	0	35
N.	81	0	45	0	0
O.	0	0	32	0	28
P.	64	0	72	72	0
Q.	48	0	42	0	0
R.	56	63	0	54	49
S.	0	0	56	40	0
T.	63	27	0	0	36

TEST 4. DIVISION

90 Basic Division Facts

	(a)	(b)	(c)	(d)	(e)
A.	2	5	3	3	2
B.	5	4	7	4	5
C.	6	8	2	4	3
D.	2	6	8	4	3
E.	6	7	7	4	5
F.	7	6	3	7	6
G.	5	5	8	2	9
H.	9	9	4	8	2
I.	3	6	8	8	9
J.	1	1	9	1	1
K.	9	1	7	1	
L.	2	3	3	2	4
M.	2	8	9	5	5
N.	0	7	4	0	3
O.	5	0	8	0	9
P.	0	6	0	4	0
Q.	6	9	0	8	7
R.	0	6	1	7	1
S.	1				

TEST 5. MISCELLANEOUS

100 of the most difficult Addition, Subtraction, Multiplication and Division Facts

	(a)	(b)	(c)	(d)	(e)
A.	11	7	42	12	6
B.	9	0	5	7	8
C.	12	4	63	13	17
D.	13	9	0	24	7
E.	0	6	8	54	56
F.	6	11	11	1	0
G.	13	0	7	9	49
H.	13	0	9	54	5
I.	7	0	27	40	1
J.	6	12	14	14	15
K.	8	5	0	8	1
L.	9	6	8	42	56
M.	0	15	9	9	0
N.	9	36	0	9	7
O.	77	7	8	72	120
P.	48	121	8	132	11
Q.	5	84	9	96	10
R.	6	110	88	11	132
S.	99	7	12	144	10
T.	4	60	9	12	108

Test 6. Graded Addition

	(*a*)	(*b*)	(*c*)	(*d*)	(*e*)	(*f*)	(*g*)	(*h*)
A.	17	19	18	19	25	29	26	21
B.	97	87	96	58	168	558	787	669
C.	28	21	23	26	64	64	95	76
D.	118	159	178	131	40	87	93	96
E.	1008	248	957	1579	125	124	116	151
F.	173	210	179	173	1394	1771	1253	1394
G.	222	312	609	1950	924	1565	1024	2535
H.	51							
I.	62							

Test 7. Graded Subtraction

	(*a*)	(*b*)	(*c*)	(*d*)	(*e*)	(*f*)	(*g*)	(*h*)
A.	95	53	83	30	23	56	68	75
B.	131	155	256	235	4	1	6	2
C.	69	58	39	78	15	5	39	19
D.	313	518	254	728	289	505	9	88
E.	50	100	23	14	109	201	129	1
F.	62	156	374	191	69	555	2678	1314
G.	105	309	508	707	684	698	596	97

Test 8A. Graded Multiplication

	(*a*)	(*b*)	(*c*)	(*d*)	(*e*)	(*f*)
A.	88	155	126	455	1,269	2,448
B.	3,555	1,686	360	909	3,200	45,050
C.	162	85	112	133	684	688
D.	576	348	936	742	88,550	56,032
E.	4,176	46,156	1,144,164	7,871,535	748	1,612
F.	7,332	3,648	7,760	5,040	2,370	5,040
G.	8,100	5,076,000	8,000	70,000	28,497	40,500

Test 8B. Graded Multiplication

	(*a*)	(*b*)	(*c*)
H.	55,680	17,545	15,096
I.	76,128	10,300	36,420
J.	316,404	218,154	145,340
K.	2,302,951	4,283,400	

Test 9. Graded Simple Division

	(a)	(b)	(c)	(d)
A.	11	42	32	111
B.	341	211	232	1,213
C.	302	403	210	230
D.	200	300	100	200
E.	303	906	904	607
F.	6 r.3	6 r.5	8 r.8	8 r.5
G.	7 r.1	24 r.1	9 r.8	9 r.3
H.	31 r.1	41 r.3	21 r.2	21 r.2
I.	41 r.3	63 r.3	87 r.1	51 r.8
J.	82 r.2	124 r.1	692 r.2	796 r.1
K.	3,705 r.3	5,071 r.2	7,001 r.3	34,207 r.5

Test 10. Long Division (easy steps)

	(a)	(b)	(c)	(d)
A.	2	3	2	4
B.	2 r.2	3 r.3	2 r.1	4 r.6
C.	2 r.3	4 r.17	2 r.12	3 r.5
D.	2 r.8	2 r.9	3 r.3	2 r.8
E.	6	4	4	3
F.	3 r.10	2 r.1	4 r.4	3 r.2
G.	21	23	28	34
H.	78 r.1	64 r.3	81 r.3	63 r.7
I.	70	50	50	50

Test 11. Long Division (harder steps)

	(a)	(b)	(c)	(d)
A.	20 r.3	32 r.9	62 r.3	70 r.6
B.	3	4	6	4
C.	9	7 r.10	7 r.23	9 r.3
D.	47	34	65 r.22	41
E.	459	379 r.13	189	608
F.	708	39 r.9	840 r.19	807 r.8

Test 12. Graded Mental Arithmetic

1. 12	9. 1/8	17. 2/-	25. 15	33. £1 : 2 : 6
2. 12	10. 16	18. 1/7½	26. 3½d.	34. 48 inches
3. 10	11. 21	19. 2 lbs.	27. 42	35. 150 yards
4. 14	12. 35	20. 3/6	28. 1½d.	36. 51 inches
5. 12	13. 9	21. 3/6	29. 3½d.	37. 1/10½
6. 6	14. 12	22. 6/1½	30. 15	38. 34
7. 18	15. 47	23. £1 : 13 : 0	31. 80	39. 6.40 P.M.
8. 2½d.	16. 72	24. 3/1	32. 10.55 A.M.	40. 1/2

INDEX

Ability, arithmetical 1-33, 74
  general, 3, 5 (*see also* Intelligence)
  mathematical, 5
Ability-grouping, 40
Absence, school, 59-60, 70, 75, 131
Activity work, 13, 14, 19, 58
Adams, L. D., 57, 135, 136
Addition, 11, 12, 21, 22, 23, 24, 52, 82, 83, 84
  column and horizontal, 94
  combinations, 56, 65, 82, 89, 118, 138-9, 146, 147, 155, 159, 181
  common errors, 123-4
  graded test, 82-5, 91-5, 115, 120, 173
  methods, 47, 55
  relationship with subtraction, 140
  upward, 47
Apparatus, 60
Areas, 19, 25, 27, 42
Arithmetic, accuracy in, 10, 21, 24, 32, 44, 49, 50, 51, 59, 61, 64, 71, 75, 77, 80, 90, 108-9, 122, 154
  achievement (attainment), 3, 4, 8, 22-3, 24, 30, 49, 50, 65, 74, 75
  ages, 122, 130, 168-9, 181-9
  attitudes to, 4, 28-9, 45, 63, 161
  correlations, 3-4
  functional value of, 17, 44-5
  mechanical, 3, 6, 7, 18, 21, 31, 32, 38, 169, 175
  mental (oral), 3, 6, 13-14, 24, 68, 69, 106, 160, 186
  practice, 10, 21-2, 24, 89
  pre-school knowledge of, 8
  problem, 3, 6, 7, 13-14, 15, 18, 21, 23, 24, 25, 26, 29, 31, 35, 38, 169, 175-7
  sets, 40, 65, 111
  tests of (*see* Tests)
Attention, 30, 69-70, 124
Australian Council for Educational Research, 37, 38

Backwardness in arithmetic, 8, 29-32, 56-73, 116-17, 118-21, 124-7, 132-79
Ballard, P. B., 59, 137
Barakat, M. K., 5, 30
Basic combinations (*see* Number combinations)
  subjects, 13
Blackwell, A. M., 5
Borrowing, 47, 51-2, 55, 65, 69, 78-9, 89, 96, 97, 98, 125, 126, 172
Bridging (tens), 85, 149
Brownell, W. A., 36, 46, 51, 55, 138
Brueckner, L. J., 36, 139
Burt, C., 28, 38, 76
Burton, W. H., 46
Buswell, G. T., 138

Calendar, 163
Capacity sums, 19
Carrying (addition), 65, 69, 70, 81, 89, 93, 94, 100
  errors, 95
  figures, 31, 103, 124
Case studies—John M., 168-70
  Kathleen D., 71
  Kenneth R., 98-9
  Ruth S., 95
Checking, 71, 175
Clark, MacKnight, 138
Class sections, 65, 75
Clocks, 163
Cobbler game, 155
Combinations, basic, 10, 21, 22, 36, 42, 90 (*see also* Number combinations)
Computation, 18, 21, 23, 24, 29, 175
Concentration, 59, 64, 69-70, 74, 84
Concepts, number, 8, 9, 13, 35, 136
Concrete material, 8, 10, 11, 37, 42, 57, 60, 62, 84, 92, 129-30, 134, 161, 177
Control groups, 50
Coombs, C. H., 6
Correlation, 3-4, 6, 30
Counters, 10, 24, 60, 61, 129-30, 135, 141, 144, 163
Counting, 8, 9-11, 12, 57, 143
  aids to, 10, 84
Co-variance, analysis of, 23
Cracknell, S. H., 144

Cross classification, 62 (*see also* Arithmetic sets)
Crutch figures, 10, 38, 54-5
Curr, W., 36
Curriculum, arithmetic (*see* Syllabus)
Cushman, L., 138

Decimals, 21, 54, 81
Decomposition (subtraction), 47-54, 78, 173
Diagnosis of difficulties, 74-83, 129-131
Diagnostic arithmetic tests (in general), 32, 75-81
Diagnostic Arithmetic Tests (Schonell), 60, 69, 82-112, 164
  addition, 82-5, 88-9, 90, 91-5
  answers, 190-4
  division, 87-9, 90, 102-6
  instructions, 106-9, 122
  interpretation of results, 113-31
  marking, 109-10
  mental arithmetic, 106
  multiplication, 86-7, 88-9, 90, 99-102
  scores, 91, 109, 122
    average, 113-17, 181-9
  scoring, 109-10, 122
  subtraction, 85-6, 88-9, 90, 96-9
  times, 108-9, 122
    average, 113, 114, 118-21
  uses of, 111
Disability (arithmetical), 5, 59, 63, 70
Dislike of arithmetic, 29, 72
Dividend, 103-6
Division, 21, 22, 23, 34, 36, 37, 38, 42, 54, 55, 60
  combinations, 56, 82, 87, 89, 118, 184
  common errors, 88, 128, 169
  graded test, 82, 102, 116, 121, 173, 188
  long, 35, 36, 54, 82, 103-6, 116-7, 121, 172-3, 189
  relation to multiplication, 141
  remainders, 88
  tables, 143, 144, 146, 152, 156, 168
Divisor, 103
  trial, 105, 106, 172
Drill, 22, 24, 44, 62, 85, 92, 135, 145, 149, 153, 178
Drummond, M., 58

Emotional attitudes, 4, 21, 24, 28-32, 58, 70-2, 74, 80
  instability, 69, 71
Emotional attitudes (*continued*)
  stability, 6, 30-1, 74
Equal addition (subtraction) 47-54, 61, 78, 173
Errors, addition, 83-4, 123-4
  arithmetic, 26, 32, 41, 44, 55, 56, 62, 69, 71, 75, 76, 80-1, 83-4, 95, 133, 152, 169, 171
  division, 128
  multiplication, 126-7
  subtraction, 125-6
Everyday arithmetic, 17-18, 39, 44-5, 161, 177
Experience, 8-9, 11-19, 21, 24, 57

Factor analysis, 4-5, 27
Factor, general, 5
Failure in arithmetic, 8, 13, 19, 29, 30, 31, 32, 34, 54, 58, 60, 65, 69, 70, 71
Fatigue, 59, 107
Flash cards, 135
Formal work, 57, 58
Four rules, 10, 58, 81, 90, 131, 165, 171
Fowler, H. M., 140
Fractions, 21, 35, 37, 63, 65, 81
Freeman, G. W. A., 29

Games (number), 57, 60, 62, 129, 153-8
Grading examples, 5, 41, 59, 66
Gray, M., 137, 138, 141
Grossnickle, F. E., 46, 139

Hackett, T. A., 46
Higher decade addition, 84-5, 149-150, 159
  in multiplication, 85, 150
Higher decade subtraction, 86
  in division, 151
Hume, E. G., 137

Imagery, 14, 26, 68, 69
Inaccuracy, 21, 30, 31, 55, 59, 65, 71, 129
Individual differences, 28
  help, 32, 41, 60, 153, 179
  work, 39, 60, 153, 132-79
Intelligence, general, 3, 5-7, 13, 14, 18, 21, 22, 31, 35, 175, 177, 179
  quotient, 15, 36, 49, 50
  tests of, 3, 15, 35, 67
Interest, 30, 31, 39, 44, 68, 70

Jacobson, E. W., 46

John, L., 138
Johnson, J. T., 49, 50

Learning, incidental, 8, 9, 11
Levels, age, 35, 37, 61
Lotto, 155

Marking, 109
Mathematics, teaching of, 46
Maturation, 20
McConnell, T. R., 42
Meaning of arithmetic, 44, 45, 51, 52, 53
Measures, 27, 106
Measuring, 14, 55, 57
Meddleton, I. G., 22-3
Mellige, H. O., 36
Memorisation, 5, 35, 42, 68-9, 86
Memory, rote, 4, 24
Mensuration, 26, 35
Mental age, 35-6, 49, 50, 57
Methods of teaching, 12, 28, 41, 44, 46-55, 62, 63-7
 of working, 80
Minuend, 53, 78, 79, 96, 97, 173
Models, 27
Monroe, S., 46
Montessori material, 136
Morfitt, M. D. K., 166
Morrison, J., 46
Morton, D. M., 27
Morton, R. L., 137, 138, 139, 141
Moser, H. E., 51, 52, 55
Multiplicand, 100, 101, 102
Multiplication, 21, 22, 23, 34, 37, 38, 42
 common errors, 87, 126-7, 169
 compound, 61-2
 graded test, 99-102, 116, 120, 173, 187
 methods, 61
 tables (combinations), 56, 69, 86-7, 89, 119, 141-2, 144, 146, 156, 157, 168, 183
Multiplier, 102
Murray, J., 49, 50

New Guinea, 15
New South Wales Education Department, 12
New Zealand Education Department, 12
Number, cardinal values, 9
 cards, 156, 157
 charts, 158-60
 combinations, 10, 21, 24, 49, 80, 90, 129, 130, 139

Number (*continued*)
 concepts, 8, 9, 10, 15, 57, 58, 129, 134, 136-7, 145
 facts, relative difficulty, 139-40
 forms, 27
 group values, 10, 11, 57, 134
 grouping, 135-6
 matching, 9, 12
 meaning of, 10, 13
 relationships, 9, 11-12, 42, 44, 48, 51, 67-8, 86, 134-5, 139, 171

Omission of figures, 69, 70, 124
Organisation, class, 39-41

Papua, 15
Percentages, 21, 65, 81
Persistence, 29, 30, 32, 35, 74
Phillips, A. J., 140
Physical states, 31, 58-9, 69
Pictorial form, 137-8
Practical work, 13, 19, 27, 42, 43, 44, 63, 167
Practice, 59, 89, 176
 material, 22, 23, 24, 145, 147
Prevention, 62
Primary school syllabus, 7, 12, 14, 26, 29, 34-7, 38, 44
Problem solving, 14, 16, 67-8, 175-7
Problems (*see also* Arithmetic, problem)
 one-step, 18, 176
 two-step, 18, 176-7
 types, 13, 176
Processes, arithmetic, 21, 36, 38, 63, 75, 135
 four, 41, 54, 65, 122
Projects, 13, 17, 39, 44-6, 161-4
Pupils, backward, 57, 75, 77, 84, 86, 94, 105, 107, 111, 134, 135, 141, 158, 164
 bright, 40, 62
 dull, 7, 10, 29, 40, 41, 55, 57, 58, 59, 63, 65, 67, 75, 77, 86, 105, 111, 130, 135, 141, 175, 177
 slow, 130, 133, 166

Quotient, 31, 54, 69, 102, 103-6, 152

Reading attainment in arithmetic, 13, 18, 175
Reasoning, ability, 13, 14, 19, 21, 30, 64, 175, 176
 deductive, 6, 25
Remainders (division), 103-6, 138, 148, 152

Remedial education centre, 30, 133
teaching 85, 92 111, 132-79
teaching material, 95, 99, 100, 104, 129, 132-79
Renwick, E. M., 61, 171
Repetition, 12, 22, 42
Research results, 34-55, 82, 152, 153
Roscoe, G. T., 15-16

Schaaf, W. L., 138
Schonell, F. E., 81, 180
Schonell, F. J., 40, 60, 69, 77, 81, 85, 86, 141, 144, 150
Schools, American, 44
Australian, 37, 38
grammar, 17, 29
infant, 58, 60, 87, 111, 134
junior, 7, 24, 60, 63, 111, 114
London, 22
primary, 37, 153
secondary modern, 7, 17, 29, 111, 114
technical, 29
Scottish Council for Research in Education, 6, 9, 36, 46, 49, 50, 55, 139
Senses, kinaesthetic, 11
tactile, 11
Sex differences in arithmetic, 28, 32-3
Shakespeare, J. J., 28
Shopping, 14, 164, 167
Signs, 11, 12
Sleight, G. F., 77
Smith, Thyra, 136
Social arithmetic, 39, 44-5
Spatial ability, 4, 26-7
knowledge, 8
Speed, 24, 49, 50, 51, 61, 71, 75, 77, 90, 108-9, 122
Springstun, E., 138
Square root, 54, 63
Standards, 37-8
Subtraction, 11, 12, 21, 22, 23, 34, 55, 77-9
additive, 48-51
combinations, 12, 56, 77, 82, 85-6, 89, 119, 138, 139, 146, 160, 182
Subtraction (*continued*)
common errors, 86, 125-6
complementary, 48-51
graded test, 76-9, 82, 96-9, 115, 120, 173, 186
methods, 47-53, 60, 61, 173
Subtrahend, 47, 53, 78, 79, 96, 97, 173
Sutherland, J., 6, 14
Syllabus (arithmetic), 6, 34-9, 62-3, 64
Symbols, abstract, 11, 12, 96

Tables, arithmetic, 3, 21, 24, 26, 42 (*see also* Combinations, Multiplication and Division)
Teachers' attitudes, 72, 80
Temperament, 4, 21, 29, 31, 71, 74
Testing, differential, 49
Tests, 19, 35, 38
attainment, 76-7
diagnostic (*see* Diagnostic arithmetic tests)
mechanical arithmetic, 77
Textbooks, 5, 14, 29, 41, 44, 137, 138, 144, 153
Thiele, C. L., 42, 139
Transfer of training, 34-5, 38, 42, 64, 149
Transposition of figures, 68

Units, experience (*see* Projects)
Upward addition, 47

Variance, analysis of, 5
Verbal ability, 8, 24-6
Vernon, P. E., 5, 6, 122
Victoria Education Department, 12
Visual imagery, 14, 26, 68, 69
Vocabulary, number, 8, 25-6, 136

Washburne, C. W., 35, 36, 66
Wauchope, M. L., 165
Weighing, 14, 57, 58, 164
Weights, 27, 106, 165
Wheeler, E. C., 64, 137
Wilson, G. M., 46

Zero, 82, 87, 88, 102
difficulties, 97, 98-9, 100, 101, 102, 103, 125, 128, 130, 171